U0572055

The Unending Path of Exploration

—— My Life as a Scientist

Author and Proofreader: Zhou Liwei
Translators: Zhao Dianhua, Li Weige

北京理工大学出版社
BEIJING INSTITUTE OF TECHNOLOGY PRESS

Those who succeed in science must not only have the passion to pursue the truth and the courage to question, but also must have the ambition to persevere.

Giving a relatively complete logical structure and theoretical system to the static and dynamic imaging electron optics has been the orientation of my research and the goal of my life.

Zhou Liwei

About the Author

Zhou Liwei, born in September 1932, a native of Zhuji city, Zhejiang Province, is the professor, chief expert of Beijing Institute of Technology (BIT), member of Chinese Academy of Engineering (CAE). He is the expert in electron optics and photoelectronic imaging. In 1958, he graduated from the Instrument Department of BIT, and in 1966, he received PhD degree in mathematics and physics from the Leningrad Electrical Technical Institute (LETI) in the Soviet Union. He served as the director of the teaching and research office, chairman of Academic Committee of BIT, chairman of Association of Science and Technology of BIT, honorary director of School for Basic Education of BIT, board chairman of Beijing Optical Society and member of the subject evaluation panel of the Academic Degrees Committee of the State Council.

Zhou Liwei has been engaged in teaching and scientific research in electron optics with wide beam focusing and photoelectronic imaging. He has published more than 300 scientific papers and reports, as well as 3 academic monographs and 5 books on popular science. He has trained more than 50 MD and PhD students. His monograph *Electron Optics with Wide Beam Focusing* was awarded the Chinese Books Prize in 1994, the National Books Prize (nominative prize) in 1995 and the Nation-wide Scientific Excellent Books First Prize in 1995. Achievements of Prof. Zhou Liwei in scientific research were awarded the National Science Congress Prize in 1978, the Ministry's First and Second Prizes for Science and Technology Progress in 1980, 1990, 1995 and 1996 and the Guang Hua First Prize for Science and Technology Funds in 1991. He was also twice of the winner of State Prize for Science and Technology Progress in 1991 and 1996.

In 1984, Zhou Liwei was awarded the title of national young and middle-aged expert with outstanding contributions. In 1992, he was elected as a foreign member of the St. Petersburg Academy of Engineering. In 1996, he was awarded the honorary title of national advanced worker in the weapon industry. In 1997, he was awarded the title of honorary doctorate by Samara State Aerospace University, Russia. In 1999, he was elected as a member of the Chinese Academy of Engineering. In 2000, he was elected a foreign member of the Academy of Engineering Science of Russian Federation, and in 2021 he was appointed as a foreign member of the Russian Academy of Engineering.

Abstract

This article describes some experiences of the author in his long and arduous exploration in scientific research, including his invention of the flat coil winding cart, his research on the imaging electron optics of the spherical concentric system with electrostatic focusing and imaging electron optics of the spherical concentric system with combined electromagnetic focusing, research on optimization design of curvilinear axial imaging electron optics, and research on dynamic imaging electron optics. Finally, it talks about his reflection and experience on scientific methods.

Foreword

I'm Zhou Liwei, a native of Hiding Green Hamlet, the 14th Village of Zhuji City, Zhejiang Province, China. Born in September 1932, I'm a professor of Beijing Institute of Technology, a member of the Chinese Academy of Engineering, a foreign member of Academy of Engineering Sciences of the Russian Federation, and a foreign member of Russian Academy of Engineering. In 1958, I graduated from the Instrument Department of Beijing Institute of Technology, began teaching there and became engaged in the teaching and scientific research of photoelectronic imaging technology. In November 1962, I went to study in the Soviet Union, hoping to learn the theory and technology of electron optics related to the night vision. However, back then, the research on electron optics for wide beam focusing and imaging was in the inception stage in Russia, with only scanty explorations. Theoretically, it was still in the rut of narrow beam electron optics, without substantial progress. I had to conduct my research all by myself at the Leningrad Electrical Technical Institute (LETI) and the Shedlin Library in Leningrad (now Saint Petersburg), all rely on my own exploration, this was a hard road. In April 1966, I passed the thesis defense for PhD degree in physics and mathematics in the Soviet Union.

First of all, let me introduce myself. I came from an engineering background: the foundation of mathematics and physics is shallow and weak. My profession: low-light level night vision technology, image tubes and image intensifiers. My field of study: imaging electron optics, which requires a strong mathematical physics foundation. The scientific research I engage in should both learn from and surpass those of my predecessors. Moreover, if scientific research is to be creative and innovative, new approaches and conceptual breakthroughs must be developed. My scientific work can be summed up as follows: research on wide electron beam focusing, so that imaging electron optics has a relatively complete theoretical system.

Science is inherited, and I grew up by studying the School of Electron Optics and its works and literature in Russia, Germany, Great Britain and other countries. However, the main characteristics of science are creativity and diversity. My research on imaging electron optics is well-informed, with my own independent insights and distinctive style, and is known as "creating a scientific school."

Before talking about my research and exploration on the theory of imaging electron optics, I'd like to introduce my experience of inventing the flat coil winding cart when I was working in Huatong Electrical Machinery Factory, the public-private joint venture in Shanghai, after graduating from secondary technical school. There I had my first experience in scientific invention in my 20 years old.

Contents

I. Invention of the Flat Coil Winding Cart

In July 1951, when I was 19 years old, I graduated from National Shanghai Advanced Machinery Vocational School (now Shanghai University of Science and Technology), and was assigned to Huatong Electrical Machinery Factory, a public-private joint venture located on Zhapu Road, Shanghai. In early 1952, I was transferred from the technical department to the electric meter workshop as a technician, to assist master Wang Chuanxie, the workshop director in managing the entire workshop. At that time, I was a boy who worked hard, studied hard, loved life, and was very shy. There were hundreds of workers in the meter workshop, most of them were young female workers, about my age. The work there involved a lot of trifles, mainly in handling various issues related to management. I worked hard from morning to night every day, and my business ability improved rapidly. When I was working in the workshop, I was fortunate to have the support of master Wang Chuanxie, a skilled chief with rich experience and high prestige. I would ask him about anything that I didn't know or didn't understand.

Seen from now, the relationship between technicians and workers in Shanghai in the early days of the People's Republic of China was very harmonious. The management of the factory was keen on mobilizing the enthusiasm of the employees, encouraging them to carry out technological innovation, and provide rationalization suggestions. The factory where I worked had a set of incentives and reward system, and a committee specifically for reward review. As a result, there were enthusiastic propositions for technological innovation and rationalization proposals in the factory.

The electric meter workshop under my management had a winding group that made coils for various electric meters (voltmeters, ammeters, watt-hour meters, etc.). Most of the work involved rotating symmetrical cylindrical coils that can be wound by a winding machine. Back then, the winding of the cylindrical coil was not fully automated, and the hand wheel of the winding machine had to be manually turned, but after all, the labor intensity was not high, and the efficiency was relatively high. However, there were also flat single-layer coils that are used on the resistor plates of 110 – volt voltmeters, which could not be wound with a winding machine, and had to be manually wound by workers. Without the assistance of machines, the manual operation had very low efficiency. It usually took 15 minutes to wind one coil. Each day, five workers had to be assigned to the winding group to meet the needs of the assembly group. More difficultly, the enameled wires had to be arranged closely and evenly, and they were on the watch for the density of the arranged enameled wires all the time, and could not relax for a moment. The labor intensity was very high, and their eyesight were suffered and damaged. At that time, I was very sympathetic of them, and thought that inventing a winding cart would not only improve efficiency, but also protect the eyes of those workers.

Master Wang Chuanxie, the workshop director, told me that all attempts to wind flat coils on the existing winding cart had failed because it was simply impossible to arrange the very thin enameled wires closely one by one on the coil stand. I couldn't help but thought this problem. It suddenly occurred to me that the principle of screw precession might be feasible, because rotating the screw to make the object connected to it move forward or backward is the simplest principle in mechanics. I believed that it was completely possible to use the precession of the screw to arrange the wires. That is to say, using the rotation of the screw, the enameled wire could be leaned against the teeth of the screw thread, so that it would be tightly arranged when the screw was turned. The problem of uniform and tight arrangement of enameled wires could be solved with appropriate pitch and screw rotation speed.

I was convinced that the principle of using the screw precession in winding would be feasible. This idea was supported by the director Mr. Wu Lüti, engineer Chen Kangde from the Technology Department, and master Wang Chuanxie, the workshop director, who encouraged me to experiment. So, I tried to draw the general assembly drawing of the flat coil winding cart. First of all, I had to address the problem of resistor sheet fixture for clamping the flat coil. My idea was that a spring sheet must be installed in the fixture, so that the flat coil resistor sheet could be rotated smoothly, mounted firmly and removed easily. In general, it was not very difficult to mount and remove the flat coil resistor chip fixture or design and manufacture the chassis of the winding cart. The difficulty consisted in choosing the appropriate screw to make the enameled wire leaning on it precede and become closely arranged. Because my design was not a planned task in the factory, so after its completion, I had to go to various workshops to find materials and asked the workers to help me with additional processing. When the workers learnt of my plan to improve production efficiency and solve the problem of eye fatigue and injury of workers, they all cordially extended a helping hand, helping me find materials, and processing them. I first asked them to process a steel screw for me, but later found that it wore on the enameled wire, so I chose hard wood and asked them to lathe a few screws with different pitches for testing. After all the parts were made and processed, I mounted the frame of the winding cart on the base, installed the loading and unloading fixtures at both ends, and connected the screw to the hand-wheel and the matching gear. Then, I asked master Le Shengzhang, the leader of the winding group, to do the test with me. Unexpectedly, the first testing was basically successful. It showed that my principle and concept of the winding cart were feasible. Master Le Shengzhang and I were very happy. Later, I made improvements to the flat coil winding cart based on suggestions made, and did two more tests, all of which were very successful. In this way, the flat coil winding cart I developed was quickly finalized and promoted in the production line. Tests showed that it took only 2 minutes to wind a flat coil with the new winding cart, indicating that the production efficiency was increased by a factor of 7.5. Originally, it took 5 workers to wind the wire, but now only one was enough. The winding quality was also improved. Even more satisfactorily, the winding with the screw was neat and beautiful, while preventing damages to the workers' eyes and eliminating the occasional loose and uneven wire arrangement that came with manual winding. In May and June 1952, two newspapers in Shanghai made special reports on my invention. In March 2011, the Shanghai Library found the *Labor Daily* dated June 18, 1952, and it carried a report (Fig. 1) on my technological innovation in Huatong Electrical Machinery Factory, a public-private partnership in Shanghai, specifically mentioning that it had improved the work efficiency by 7.5 times. I had not turned 20 then.

When the flat coil winding cart was materialized, everyone felt that the idea of using the screw for winding wire was ingenious and very clever. The cart was simple and practical, and the idea of screw precession won unanimous praise. All the workers thought it the best solution for this problem. Previously they were at a loss and didn't know

装一只绕線車
工作快七倍半

華通電機廠一一〇伏電壓表的電阻片，是扁平的單層線圈，一直用手工繞，十五分鐘才能繞一只。繞線組每天要五個人繞，才能供應上裝配小組需要。繞線組長樂生章老師傅和技術員周立偉研究，並請電表工程師協助，輕過三次研究試驗，終於創造了一只新的繞線車，二分鐘就可繞一只，比原來快七倍半。（陳廣恬、王興昌）

Fig. 1   Zhou Liwei's invention of the flat coil winding
cart reported in *Labor News* dated **June 18, 1952** in
Shanghai

what to do; when they saw that the problem of manual wiring was solved with only one screw, they found that there wasn't anything extraordinary about it. The principle and mechanical structure were simple and familiar! Yes, they were not unusual at all. In fact, that is the way many technological innovations or inventions seem.

Later, when I read a book on scientific methods, I realized that I had actually used a method called "simple analogy" there. It used here is, when the screw is turned, the nut sleeved on it moves left and right—that is the simplest principle in mechanism. Likewise, the enameled wire rested on the nut or the teeth of the screw would swing left and right and move ahead, accordingly. In fact, the lathe I saw every day in the factory had a turning tool that used screw precession to cut the parts and components, in the manner of doing subtraction; similarly, the flat coil winding cart also used screw precession to wind the enameled wire to the frame, in the manner of doing addition. This is a simplest analogy. The principle is the same, but the scenario of application was different. This principle is usually not noticed, but once it is exposed, everyone understands it. I later concluded that innovation occurs when you put forth an idea and materialize it where no one else notices—perhaps in the most common place. Therefore, innovation is not mysterious, nor is it necessarily complicated. Sometimes it is so simple. The key is dedication and perseverance!

The invention of the flat coil winding cart shows that those whoever love innovation and become passionate about it is likely to succeed. Back then, I was young and had no advanced knowledge or training. All I had was a degree from a secondary technical school. It can be seen that neither age nor knowledge matters in innovation. It is not a patent of people with higher education and profound knowledge: they are not the only ones qualified for innovating or succeeding in innovation. In fact, all of us can give play to our ingenuity on the basis of the existing culture in our own jobs, keep up with our exploration, persist in what we want to do, and constantly seek improvements. That way, we are likely to succeed in inventing and creating something. Admittedly, people with rich and profound knowledge tend to think more deeply, and have greater chances of achieving success in innovation. Many original results and scientific achievements have been made by knowledgeable scientists and experienced engineers. Therefore, those who want to innovate still need to learn more and practice more, so as to enrich their knowledge, improve their thinking, enhance their capacities, and become more resourceful.

Seeing from that invention of mine, although I was young at that time, I didn't have much knowledge, and I didn't know anything about scientific methods, nor did I know the term "analog." However, when I saw that the lathe was doing subtraction in cutting parts, it immediately occurred to me that the principle might be used for designing the winding cart. The capabilities were the same, but the subtraction had to be switched to addition. Later I came to know the term "analogical reasoning." The so-called analogical reasoning is a logical method to deduce that two or two types of objects may be similar or the same in other aspects based on the similarity or similarity in some aspects. That is to say, it takes other things as a starting point to think about one's own business similarly, which is the usual way for human beings to acquire new knowledge and new inspiration, and it is also the best way. Association and analogy are human instincts and innate abilities. Those who are engaged in technology will benefit greatly if they can transform this spontaneous talent into a conscious ability and apply it flexibly.

In my opinion, no matter what type of innovation, as an individual, when creating, it requires knowledge, wisdom and ability, and more importantly, curiosity and enterprising spirit. Recall the process of the birth of the flat coil winding cart, which is a very common technological innovation, but it contains the elements of innovation: the basic is "knowledge" that I learned about screws at the National Shanghai Advanced Machinery Vocational School is the foundation, and the association thinks about the idea of screw processing enameled wire and applies it to practice is "wisdom," design and production of flat coil winding cart requires "ability," curiosity, perseverance and hard work are "spirit." Knowledge-wisdom-abilities-spirit these are the four basic elements that individuals must have when they innovate. The four are organically combined and innovation is born.

My technological invention won me praise from my companions, who said that I had been so kind and that my sympathy and compassion for the female colleagues toiling in winding the flat coils had made it possible for me to achieve the technological innovation. It also greatly endeared me to my fellow workers, enhanced my reputation, and earned me praise from the factory leaders and the technical department. In the subsequent professional eligibility review, I was directly promoted from the second level assistant technician to the fourth level technician. My salary was increased to 74.5 yuan a month, plus a monthly bonus of more 20 yuan. In the early 1950s, the monthly income of nearly 100 yuan was by all means a fortune.

By the way, some episodes that happened at that time show my naivety and ignorance. After I made a fortune from the invention of the flat coil winding cart, I made two sets of gabardine tunic suits, bought a watch and a famous British bicycle, and bought a lot of novels. My father also asked someone to build a bookcase at home. I also went to the highest 24th-floor International Hotel on Nanjing Road in Shanghai to have a western meal, paid 1 yuan, and opened a foreign meat dish. Anyway, I was so happy then.

One day, when I went to work in the factory, I was very proud of wearing a straight tunic suit. After arriving at the factory, I found that people were staring at me with strange eyes. At that time, there were two first-class engineers in the factory, Prof. Gu Guotong and Prof. Jiang Gonghui. They were both big names in China's electrical machinery industry and technical authorities. They were just like the engineers or technicians in the factory. Their clothes are very simple, and many people's clothes have been patched. At that time, I felt that it was really shameful for me to show off in the factory. When I got home, I hurriedly took off my tunic suit and never wore it again. When I went to study in Beijing Institute of Technology, I brought these two sets of Chinese tunic suits, but never wore them because they were too conspicuous. When the "communism wind" was blowing in the 1950s, my two sets of Chinese tunic suits were turned over by my classmates and turned out to be the public property of communists. I forgot about this. Once at a gathering of old classmates in Beijing, my classmate Mao Zhicheng mentioned this incident and said that my Chinese tunic suit was taken as public properties by classmates, and I was very generous, and it doesn't hurt at all.

About that fancy bike from England, I rode it to work with great pride. Afraid of being stolen by others after returning home, my father carried it to my home on the 3rd floor. At that time, the house I lived in was renovated from a hotel in the southern urban area of Shanghai. There were a lot of people and it was very mixed. The corridors were very narrow and it was very dark at night. It was actually similar to a slum. Many people jokingly called the place that I lived in was "72 Tenant" (the name of a movie at the time). My house faced south on the 3rd floor. There were 3 small rooms, each of which was less than 10 square meters. There was a small loft and a balcony by the street, at that time, it was the best home in the whole building. But there were no kitchen, no toilet and no water in the house. The corridor was very narrow and it was very dark at night, so be careful when walking up and down.

I remember that there was no public lighting in the upper and lower corridors at that time, and each family installed a small light bulb on the corridor to make it easier for their family members to get up and down. If the house does not have its own lighting, it can only fumble up and down on its own. Under these conditions, my father had to carry my bike up and down every day. My mother was not satisfied with me. She said, "Your dad will carry your bicycle downstairs in the morning, wait for you downstairs at night, carrying the bike up to our home, think about how hard he is!" Immediately, I seemed to realize in my conscience that I was too confused, and that my happiness was based on my father's hard work. After 2 days, I resold my bike, never rode a bike again, and took the bus to work.

As for the watch, it was definitely a parallel import and the watch stopped in a few days. I asked someone to repair it, and it went back and forth and couldn't come back.

Besides, there is one more thing to talk about. One day, Mr. Wu Lüti, the leader of the technical department of the factory and my immediate supervisor asked me, "How do you spend so much money?" I said, "now my father is working, my sister was married, and my younger brother worked as an apprentice long before the founding of new China, and my family didn't ask me to pay. " Mr. Wu said, "You cannot be so young. Your salary is to be kept by your parents. If you need anything, you can ask them for it. " Mr. Wu was right, so I gave my salary to my mother.

These are some episodes that happened when I was young. Looking back at that time, my strengths were self-motivation and shame, and I would correct my mistakes.

Here, by the way, I came out of the factory and went to university. After graduation, I stayed on the campus as a teaching assistant. Then I studied abroad and got PhD degree in physics and mathematics in the Soviet Union. Later, I became an associate professor and full professor. However, from the early 1950s to the early 1980s, it lasted for 30 years, my salary has not reached the level of when I was a technician in Shanghai Huatong Electrical Machinery Factory.

Kropotkin once said, "As long as a person experiences the joy of scientific creation once in his life, he will never forget it. " The invention of the flat coil winding cart was my first attempt at technological invention, and in retrospect it is of course naive, but this incident planted the seeds of my love for scientific research. It also motivates me move towards higher goals. I've made up my mind that I'm going to college and have more knowledge. On October 1953, I was admitted to the Beijing Institute of Technology, which started my path of scientific exploration.

II. Research on Imaging Electron Optics of the Concentric Spherical System with Electrostatic Focusing

In July 1958, I graduated from Beijing Institute of Technology and stayed on as a teaching assistant, engaged in teaching and research of photoelectronic imaging technology. My area of research was the electron optics of various image tubes and image intensifiers, a branch of charged particle optics. Charged particle optics is a very broad subject area, and there are a plethora of books and papers. In November 1962, when I went to the Soviet Union to further my scholarship, I almost browsed all monographs and literatures on the subject published by experts in the field of electron optics in the Leningrad Shedlin library and the library of the Soviet Academy of Sciences. In the 1960s, the copier was not invented, and I didn't have a camera, so I copied everything by hand. Of course, the progress was very slow, but it was quite rewarding. When taking notes, I was always on the lookout for topics that made worthwhile and feasible research topics. For a long time. I have been groping my way through the tunnels of science, looking for my way to the light. Although it was very difficult, I was not discouraged.

I remember when I did the first bibliographic excerpt in the Shedlin Library, I wrote some words: "Воля + Терпение + Метод = Успех" — meaning "ambition + patience + method = success" on the cover of the notebook. Those words became the motto of my scientific research during my stay in the Soviet Union. Looking back now, I find that my engrossment in studying the literature on charged particle optics of various Soviet schools in the Leningrad Shedlin Library was quite enlightening and rewarding.

However, in the early 1960s, whether it was in Europe and the US or the Soviet Union, the research on imaging electron optics was just in its infancy. The only papers on the topic were mostly based on the routine of narrow beam geometrical electron optics, and the focus was the third-order geometrical lateral aberration. I clearly remember that there were several articles impressive to me at that time, written by A. Recknagel (1941) from Germany, P. Schagen (1952) from the UK, E. Ruska (1933) from Germany, Л. А. Арцимович (1944), Крупп Д М (1962), Sherman (Семан О. И) (1955) from the Soviet Union, Ximen Jiye (1957) from China and others. A. Recknagel and P. Schagen gave the expression of the circle of confusion on the limiting image plane for the electrons emitted from the center of the cathode surface of the electrostatic cathode lens, and Л. А. Арцимович gave the expression for the radius of the circle of least confusion at the optimal image plane. Крупп Д М gave the expression of the radius of the circle of confusion at the Gaussian image plane of the concentric spherical system, and Ximen Jiye was a pioneer in the research on the aberration theory of the combined electromagnetic cathode lens. E. Ruska, the Nobel laureate and inventor of the electron microscope, was the first to study the concentric spherical system with electrostatic focusing. He gave me a lot of inspiration. I even translated the relevant chapters of his dissertation from German into Russian. In order to understand the original papers, I taught myself German specifically for that purpose.

Imaging electron optics involves such issues as large object surface and imaging with wide beam focusing, while the theory of narrow electron beam focusing and imaging conventionally studied by electron optics was not applicable for studying electron optics of wide electron beam imaging devices. So, I mainly thought about two questions.

(1) The applicability of existing theories and methods in paraxial narrow beam electron optics cannot be used to solve the electron optical problem of wide electron beam imaging. The paraxial electron optics theory can only address the ideal imaging, and be applied for solving the electron optics problems in the area adjacent to the symmetry axis. Imaging electron optics means studying the traveling trajectories of the electron beams with large object surface width emitting from the photocathode in the system, as well as the law of imaging and the aberrations formed. However, in previous studies, the spatial potential was usually expressed by the Scherzer expansion of the potential distribution on the axis, with considerable deviation from the actual situation. The existing theories, methods and means were still insufficient for solving practical problems. In particular, new approaches should be explored for focusing and imaging of off-axis electron beams.

(2) How should the lateral aberration of the imaging electron optics be defined? Back then, the academic circles of electron optics at home and abroad were studying the third-order (geometrical) lateral aberration of the imaging electron optics, which was generally believed to be the main factor affecting imaging quality in devices. However, the concept was inferred from narrow beam electron optics and was not proven. There was no clear conclusion on whether the third-order geometric lateral aberrations were the only type of lateral aberration in imaging electron optics.

"The way ahead is long and has no ending; yet high and low I'll search with my will unbending." said by great ancient poet Qu Yuan. I knew that the path ahead will be long and difficult, but I was clear and determined about the direction of my quest.

In scientific research, determining where to start is the key to the solution. I spent a long time thinking about the issue. Eventually, it dawned on me that if I could find an ideal model yielding analytical solutions for imaging electron optics, I would begin with it, and thoroughly study its imaging laws, actual trajectories and paraxial trajectories, so as to have a correct understanding and grasp of ideal imaging and lateral aberration. That way, there would be guidance for the general theory and design of the electron optical system with electrostatic focusing. Ultimately, I chose the trajectory of electron motion in a bi-electrode concentric spherical system with electrostatic focusing as the entry point for my research. I thought that if an analytical solution to the imaging position of this model can be found and expressed as a series expansion, it will be possible to address such issues as ideal imaging and define lateral aberrations in imaging electron optical systems.

The trajectory of electrons traveling in the concentric sphere was first studied by the famous German scholar E. Ruska in 1933. The British scientist P. Schagen continued the research in 1951. In examining this system, I thought that the emphasis in studying the focus and imaging of its electron trajectories should not only be on the trajectories of electrons traveling inside the concentric spheres, but also on the point of intersection where the electron traveling through the anode of the system converges with the axis as the electron beams travel from the axial point through them. The location of this drop point has to be precise because it has the largest influence on the imaging properties and aberrations of the electron optical system. Therefore, I focused my research on the trajectory of the electrons traveling from the axial point after passing through the anode of the concentric spherical system and their precise position when they reach the image plane, to study the electron beam envelope between the limiting image plane and the Gaussian image plane, and the diameter of the circle of confusion formed on each image plane.

Fig. 2 is the calculation diagram of the trajectory and imaging of electrons in the bi-electrode concentric spherical electron optical system with electrostatic focusing (concave cathode-convex anode system and convex cathode-concave anode system). I did not study the theory of electron optics abstractly, but expressed my assumptions (electron trajectory and aberration) clearly with graphics, so as to give my research a clearer direction. I drew a picture of the trajectories of electrons in the concentric spherical system to be studied, as shown in Fig. 2, as the basis for my study.

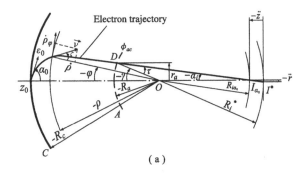

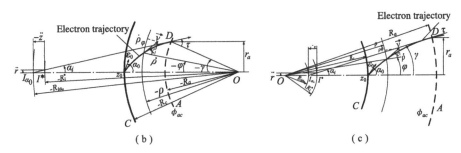

Fig. 2 Schematic diagram of imaging electron optics for bi-electrode concentric spherical system with electrostatic focusing

(a) $n > 2 \left(n = \dfrac{R_c}{R_a} \right)$ real image; (b) $2 > n > 1$ virtual image; (c) $n < 1$ virtual image

In scientific research, theorists are the most interested in pursuing the theoretical universality. However, universality must be confirmed by particularity to obtain wide recognition, and universality resides in particularity. The same is true for the study of imaging electron optics. I thought that with thorough exploration of the particularity, it would be possible to find clues with universality and regularity. In this way, starting from the particularity to study special types of wide electron beam focusing and imaging became a breakthrough for me to study the imaging electron optics. Therefore, the bi-electrode electrostatic concentric spherical system, that is, the ideal model of electrostatic cathode lens, was an entry point for my research on imaging electron optics.

My thinking at that time was to study the focusing of electron beams in the ideal model of the bi-electrode concentric spherical system, analyze and discuss the specific contradictions contained in electron beam imaging and convergence, and analyze the particularity of its contradictions as a cathode lens, to find some clues that have general significance and regularity for cathode lenses. Those clues would not only provide a theoretical basis for the study of concentric spherical imaging electron optics; but also furnish practical significance for the further study of axial symmetric cathode lens, because the contradictory particularity of the ideal model contains the contradictory universality of the wide electron beam imaging of electrostatic cathode lenses. So I felt that if I could address the particularity of imaging electron optics of the concentric spherical system, I might become clear about some of the puzzling issues in the imaging electron optics, and consolidate the foundation for studying the universality.

Admittedly, studying the particularity is aimed at seeking the law of universality. Theoretical research must also transform individual and specific knowledge into general and abstract knowledge, and must not stop at individual or special problems. The study of universal laws is the focus of scientific research. Therefore, my research idea was to begin with the easier issues before tackling the difficult ones. I decided to study the electrostatic focusing system first, and then the electromagnetic combined focusing system; study various specific imaging systems, and then general electronic optical imaging systems. From theory to design, that was how I thought about and approached the scientific problems of imaging electron optics.

In my opinion, for scientific research, the beginning point is key, but unfolding the problem after cutting in, determining the crux of the problem, proposing practical hypotheses, and giving a clear definition are even more important. I was determined to figure out the law of the electron beam's trajectory first, and find the exact location of the landing point after the electrons escaping from the object point on the axis pass through the anode. However, for scientific research, solving a couple of specific problems is not enough. I had to carry out scientific abstraction and carefully examine the imaging laws and characteristics, in order to correctly understand and grasp the determination of ideal imaging and the formation of lateral aberrations.

As for unfolding a scientific topic, as I've mentioned above, the key point of concern for me was to accurately locate the landing point where the electrons emitting from the object point of the cathode surface pass through the concentric spherical anode grid and intersect with the central axis of the system, that is, the converging point of the emitting electron beam with the axis of the system. Therefore, I had to find the point where the electron ray reaches the anode after escaping from the photocathode surface, as well as its incident angle and its exit angle from the anode. That is the same as ray tracing of the optical lens system or optical path tracing in designing the glass lens of the geometrical optical systems. This way, I would be able to determine the ideal image and the aberration of the system.

As for the bi-electrode concentric spherical system with electrostatic focusing, although it had been studied by some scientists in Germany, Great Britain, Russia and other countries, their focus was to study the trajectory of electrons moving inside the concentric spherical system, while ignoring the movement of electrons after passing through the anode. Only the approximate solution of the trajectory with zero initial velocity of the electron was obtained. Such processing was far from enough for studying the electron optical imaging characteristics of the system, since I had to obtain the precise landing point where the electrons cross the axis after emitting from the on-axis point of the cathode surface and passing through the concentric spherical system. Therefore, finding the exact solution and paraxial solution of the electron trajectory was the key of my research. Finally, I found the exact solution and paraxial solution of the imaging position of the electron trajectory emitting from the cathode in the bi-electrode and multi-electrode concentric spherical system with electrostatic focusing, and expressed it in the form of series expansion, thus solving electron optical properties such as ideal imaging and the problem of defining electron optical aberrations. In short, I started with the particularity of the contradiction in the ideal model of electron optics for the concentric spherical system with electrostatic focusing, and studied the universality of the contradiction in wide electron beam imaging to guide the in-depth study of imaging electron optics.

So, what kind of trajectory solutions did I need for studying the electron optics of a bi-electrode concentric spherical system with electrostatic focusing? I'll summarize my thinking as follows.

First of all, it is necessary to re-derive the expression of the trajectories of electrons escaping from the photocathode surface in the bi-electrode concentric spherical system. Although E. Ruska, P. Schagen and other predecessors had deduced the expression for the flight electron trajectories in the internal of the concentric spherical system, I had to find another form of trajectory expression as following:

$$\varphi = f(\rho), \quad \zeta = \psi(\rho)$$

i. e. ,

$$\sin\varphi = -\frac{(\mu - 1)(c + d_0)}{bd_0 + b_0 c}\sin\alpha_0, \cos\varphi = \frac{bc + b_0 d_0}{bd_0 + b_0 c}, \tan\zeta = \frac{\mu\sin\alpha_0}{b}$$

where

$$b_0 = \cos\alpha_0, \quad b = \left[1 + \frac{\varphi_{ac}}{\varepsilon_0}\frac{(\mu - 1)}{(n - 1)} - \mu^2\sin^2\alpha_0\right]^{1/2}$$

$$c = 1 - 2\mu(n - 1)\frac{\varepsilon_0}{\varphi_{ac}}\sin^2\alpha_0, d_0 = 1 - 2(n - 1)\frac{\varepsilon_0}{\varphi_{ac}}\sin^2\alpha_0$$

where $\mu = \dfrac{R_c}{\rho}$, $n = \dfrac{R_c}{R_a}$, R_c, R_a are the radii of curvature of spherical photocathode and spherical anode, respectively.

It can more easily determine the location of the electrons emitting from the photocathode upon arrival at the anode, the direction of the electron ray, and its intersection with the axis of the system. This is similar to the optical tracing in geometrical optics, and the result is the "actual trajectory" of the traveling electrons. The expression of the landing point from the intersection of the actual trajectory of electrons escaping from the point on the axis with the axis of symmetry is called the "actual landing point solution," of which no simplification should be made in this process. Therefore, we may obtain the precise expressions of the landing position of trajectory and its slope as following:

$$R_i = -R_a\frac{n(b_1 d_0 + b_0 c_0)}{b_1(n - 1)(c_0 + d_0) - n(b_1 c_0 + b_0 d_0)}$$

$$\tan\alpha_i = -\frac{b_1(n - 1)(c_0 + d_0) - n(b_1 c_0 + b_0 d_0)}{b_1(b_1 c_0 + b_0 d_0) + n(n - 1)(c_0 + d_0)\sin^2\alpha_0}\sin\alpha_0$$

Secondly, the expression of the "actual landing point solution" turned into a series expansion arranged in order of power is the exact solution of the actual trajectory landing point. In the expression of the "exact solution," I have to find under what conditions can the electrons escaping the axial object point be ideally imaged, that is, the law that the outgoing electrons can all converge at the same point, thus defining the "ideal imaging condition." The condition is called "paraxial condition." The electron trajectory solution obtained by the differential equation of "paraxial condition" is called "paraxial trajectory solution" or simply "paraxial solution." Therefore, we may obtain the approximate expressions of the landing position of trajectory and its slope as following:

$$R_i = -R_a \frac{n}{n-2}\left\{1 + \frac{2(n-1)}{n-2}\sqrt{\frac{\varepsilon_z}{\varphi_{ac}}} + \frac{2n(n-1)}{(n-2)^2}\frac{\varepsilon_z}{\varphi_{ac}} - \frac{2(n-1)^2}{n-2}\frac{\varepsilon_r}{\varphi_{ac}}\right\}$$

$$\tan\alpha_i = -(n-2)\sqrt{\frac{\varepsilon_r}{\varphi_{ac}}}\left\{1 - \frac{2(n-1)}{n-2}\sqrt{\frac{\varepsilon_z}{\varphi_{ac}}} + \frac{3n-2}{2(n-2)}\frac{\varepsilon_z}{\varphi_{ac}} + \frac{(n-1)(n^2-n+2)}{2(n-2)}\frac{\varepsilon_r}{\varphi_{ac}}\right\}$$

Thirdly, study the imaging of paraxial electron trajectories escaping from the photocathode with an axial initial energy of ε_{z1} $(0 \leqslant \varepsilon_{z1} \leqslant \varepsilon_{0max})$, which is called ideal imaging or "paraxial imaging." Therefore, all such paraxial electrons will converge to the same imaging point, which is also the location of the ideal imaging plane that we have to determine.

Finally, determine the electron optical lateral magnification when the initial axial energy corresponding to the electron is ε_{z1}, that is, the ratio of the image height to the object height on the ideal imaging plane corresponding to ε_{z1}.

Generally speaking, in the research of imaging electron optics, in most cases, there is no need to seek the "exact solution" of the trajectory landing point. The paraxial solution or approximate solution with sufficient precision is sufficient for determining the paraxial lateral aberration of the imaging electron optical system.

In the above description, I have made conscious efforts to define and clearly distinguish the actual solution, exact solution, paraxial solution and approximate solution of the electron trajectory, in order to strictly define the imaging characteristics and aberrations of the electron optical system in my research. None of the rest monographs and papers on imaging electron optics at home and abroad so far has made such detailed division and description of the imaging and lateral aberration of the electron trajectory escaping from the cathode surface in the electron optical imaging system. That is the fundamental point which differentiates my theory of imaging electron optics from that of other scholars.

Here, I will briefly talk about the differences between me and Russian scholars in the research on electron optics of the bi-electrode electrostatic concentric spherical system. As said above, the trajectory of electrons traveling inside the system had been solved by E. Ruska and P. Schagen in the 1930s and 1950s, but based on the spherical coordinate system according to the formula $\varphi = \varphi(\rho)$. In studying the electron optical imaging of the bi-electrode electrostatic concentric spherical system, it is necessary to transfer the description of the electron trajectory from the spherical coordinate system to the cylindrical coordinate system, which is an axial symmetrical system. Then, the central axis of the cylindrical coordinate system can be selected to coincide with the symmetrical axis of the spherical coordinate system, and the analytical expression of trajectory $r = r(z)$ can be obtained for the actual electrons escaping from the origin in the cathode surface as following:

$$r(z) = \frac{2(n-1)}{1 - 4(n-1)^2 \frac{\varepsilon_r \varepsilon_z}{\Phi_{ac}^2}} \left(\frac{\varepsilon_r}{\Phi_{ac}}\right)^{1/2} \left\{ (z + R_c) \left(\frac{\varepsilon_z}{\Phi_{ac}}\right)^{1/2} - \frac{2z(n-1)\varepsilon_z^{1/2}\varepsilon_r}{\Phi_{ac}^{3/2}} \right.$$

$$- (z + R_c) \left[\frac{- z}{(n - 1)(z + R_c)} + \frac{(z + R_c)^2 \varepsilon_z + z^2 \varepsilon_r}{(z + R_c)^2 \Phi_{ac}} \right]^{1/2} \Bigg\}$$

where $n = R_c/R_a$, which is the ratio of the radius of the cathode to the anode of the concentric spherical system; Φ_{ac} is the potential of the spherical anode relative to the spherical cathode; and $\varepsilon_r, \varepsilon_z$ represent the radial initial potential and the axial initial potential corresponding to the escaped electrons, respectively.

In 1978, I published this equation in *Engineering Optics*, a journal of Beijing Institute of Technology, and in 1993, I listed it in my monograph *Electron Optics with Wide Beam Focusing* (page 129). That is the analytical solution of the actual trajectory in the cylindrical coordinate system in the bi-electrode concentric spherical system with electrostatic focusing, without any simplification. The formula actually corrected the errors in the expressions given in some monographs on electron optics published in Russia in the 1980s. I shall not bother readers with the details here. For further understanding, readers can read my article "Imaging Electron Optics of Concentric Spherical System with Electrostatic Focusing (I) Electron Trajectory Equation of Bi-electrode Concentric Spherical System with Electrostatic Focusing" published in the 8th issue of April 2022 in *Acta Optica Sinica*, as well as three other related articles.

If the paraxial condition is introduced into my analytical expression $r = r(z)$ given above derived for the actual electron trajectory of the concentric spherical system, and ε_r/Φ_{ac} and its higher order term which is much smaller than 1 in the denominator and in the curly brackets are omitted, the paraxial trajectory $r^*(z)$ of the electrons emitted from the origin with the initial condition parameters $(\varepsilon_0, \alpha_0)$ in the cylindrical coordinate system is obtained after some sorting out, and expressed as:

$$r^*(z) = 2z\sqrt{\frac{\varepsilon_r}{\Phi(z)}}\left\{\sqrt{1 + \frac{\varepsilon_z}{\Phi(z)}} - \sqrt{\frac{\varepsilon_z}{\Phi(z)}}\right\}$$

where

$$\Phi(z) = \Phi_{ac}\frac{-z}{(n-1)(z+R_c)}$$

is an expression of the axial potential distribution of the concentric spherical system. $r^*(z)$ is called the paraxial trajectory. As an abstraction and simplification of the actual trajectory expression, it is the solution of the paraxial trajectory equation of the electrostatic cathode lens in the cylindrical coordinate system under the potential distribution on the axis of the bi-electrode concentric spherical system, and is thus called "paraxial trajectory solution." Oddly enough, the trajectory representation I derived also contains an analytical representation of the axial potential distribution $\Phi(z)$. That is an extremely rare case and the first discovery of imaging electron optics, indicating that the resulting image dispersion of the electrons escaping from the photocathode in an electrostatic imaging system at the anode aperture is indistinguishable from the projection imaging of a uniform field. Therefore, I proved theoretically that if the amount of radial initial energy of electrons escaping from the photocathode is discarded in the actual trajectory equation, and defined as satisfying the paraxial condition, it would be possible to study the ideal imaging properties and lateral aberrations of the system with the solution of the trajectory equation expressed by the second-order homogeneous ordinary differential equation. I came to this conclusion practically from an electron optical study of a bi-electrode electrostatic concentric spherical system.

It should be pointed out that in my research on imaging electron optics, I did not put the position of the ideal imaging plane at the position where the axial initial energy of the electron $\varepsilon_{z1} = 0$, or fix it at the limiting image plane position like the electron optics scholars in

Russia and the West had done. In my opinion, that approach is certainly a method and means of dealing with scientific problems in imaging electron optics, and it is not a big mistake. When Russian and Western scientists designed the image tube, they all made this assumption of $\varepsilon_{z1} = 0$. However, this treatment actually simplifies a scientific problem and loses a lot of valuable information. Therefore, it is by no means the best policy, or desirable. My research shows that for concentric spherical electron optical systems, the electron beam escaping from the photocathode surface gathers together after passing through the grid anode and to form an electron beam envelope. There is no doubt that the position of the ideal imaging plane should be the position with the circle of least confusion where the electron beam envelope converges, that is, the optimal image plane; it is not located in the limiting image plane, but in its vicinity. To this end, I derived a mathematical expression for the electron beam envelope between the limiting image plane and the Gaussian image plane, and visualized the beam convergence shape of the electron beam in the imaging segment.

In research, scientific abstraction is very important. It screens the research findings "by removing the false and keeping the truthful, and removing the dross and saving the essence." In the research on imaging electron optics, there is considerable emphasis on the clarity (or blur) of the image formed by the system. Usually it is called image aberration, that is, the deviation of the actual image from the ideal image. Only on this basis can we talk about so-called aberrations and define aberrations to study the degree of image blurring. Therefore, it is first necessary to study the conditions under which the system can be imaged ideally, that is, an object point corresponds to an image point. Only on this basis can we talk about and define aberrations to study the degree of image blurring. Therefore, it is first necessary to study how to achieve ideal imaging and what conditions must be satisfied for all electrons escaping from the object point to converge on one image point.

My research shows that for an electron optical system, if a beam of electrons escaping from the axial point of the cathode surface have the same axial initial energy, and meet the paraxial condition $\varepsilon_r/\phi_i \ll 1$, where ϕ_i is the potential of the imaging surface and ε_r is the potential corresponding to the radial initial energy of the escaped electrons, referred to as radial initial energy or radial initial potential—in other words, if the term with radial initial energy ε_r is omitted from the expansion of the electron trajectory in the equation of the landing point, the beam of electrons will converge on one point, and form an ideal image. Only then can we discuss aberrations. In a physical sense, after the photoelectrons escape from the cathode surface, the speed of its axial travelling direction will increase very quickly while their radial speed remains much the same, with extremely small changes. This assumption is physically true, and I have proved from the drop point of the obtained exact solution of the bi-electrode concentric spherical system that if we omit the terms ε_r/ϕ_i in the expansion of the solution of the actual electron trajectory, we can obtain the paraxial solution, that is, the solution of the paraxial trajectory equation. The solution corresponds to the paraxial trajectory of the electrons, indicating that they will all converge at one point somewhere on the axis.

The essence of scientific research is to find laws. As mentioned above, the position of the ideal image plane can be determined by the exact solution of the electron trajectory and the paraxial trajectory defined by it abstractly. The position corresponds to ε_{z1}, the value of the selected axial initial energy; that is the so-called ideal imaging. In other words, all paraxial electrons with the same axial initial energy escaping from the cathode surface, namely $\varepsilon_z = \varepsilon_{z1}$, no matter how different the radial initial energy ε_r is, they will always converge on one point—the ideal image point, which forms at the ideal imaging, the plane is called as ideal image plane. Therefore, other paraxial electrons whose $\varepsilon_z \neq \varepsilon_{z1}$ will form a dispersion of the image on this ideal image plane, and give rise to paraxial lateral aberration. The dispersion of the images formed by the electron trajectory that does not meet the paraxial condition on the image plane is called geometric lateral aberration. My research has shown that electrostatic electron optical imaging systems have two types of aberrations with different properties, namely paraxial aberration and geometric aberration. That is a point not recognized or not clearly recognized by preceding scientists.

From our research, the lateral aberration of axial point can be expressed by

$$\Delta r = r(z_i^*, \sqrt{\varepsilon_z}, \sqrt{\varepsilon_r}) - r^*(z_i^*, \sqrt{\varepsilon_{z1}}) = \Delta r^* + \delta r = \Delta r_2^* + \Delta r_3^* + \delta r_3$$

where

$$\Delta r_2^* = \frac{2M}{E_c} \sqrt{\varepsilon_r}(\sqrt{\varepsilon_z} - \sqrt{\varepsilon_{z1}}), \quad \Delta r_3^* = \frac{2M}{-E_c \sqrt{\phi_{ac}}} \sqrt{\varepsilon_r}(\varepsilon_z - \varepsilon_{z1})$$

$$\delta r_3 = \frac{2M}{-E_c \sqrt{\phi_{ac}}}(n-1)\varepsilon_r^{3/2}$$

Therefore, we can define the lateral aberration formed by the electron beam on the imaging plane as

The lateral aberration = the paraxial lateral aberration +

the geometric lateral aberration

while

The paraxial lateral aberration = the 2nd order paraxial lateral

chromatic aberration +

the 3rd order paraxial lateral

aberration

The geometric lateral aberration = the 3rd order geometric lateral aberration

Therefore, the total lateral aberration = the 2nd order paraxial lateral chromatic aberration + the 3rd order paraxial lateral aberration + the 3rd order geometric lateral aberration

Here, the paraxial lateral chromatic aberration is caused by the difference in the initial energy of the electrons escaping from the cathode surface, and it is tantamount to the chromatic aberration caused by different colors in light optics; the geometric lateral aberration is equivalent to geometric aberrations caused by the difference in geometric quantities in light optics.

Finally, let me summarize what new discoveries, new results and new understandings were obtained in this research.

First, a new trajectory expression of electrons escaping from the cathode surface in the concentric spherical system with electrostatic focusing was derived. Like the tracing formula for the transition of light from one refracting surface to the next one in geometric optics, it is applicable for studying not only electron optics of bi-electrode concentric spherical systems with electrostatic focusing, but also electron tracing of multi-electrode concentric sphere systems with electrostatic focusing.

Second, the exact point where the electron beam would finally converge after escaping from the cathode surface and passing through the concentric spherical system, that is, the exact solution of the electron trajectory was obtained, without any simplification. This laid a solid foundation for studying ideal imaging and defining lateral aberrations. Meanwhile, the analytical expression of the actual electron trajectory escaping from the origin of the cathode surface in the cylindrical coordinate system in the bi-electrode electrostatic concentric spherical system was given, correcting some errors in the literature.

Third, the paraxial solution of the electron trajectory in the concentric spherical system with electrostatic focusing was derived from the exact solution, and it constituted the analytical solution of the equation of electron motion or the electron trajectory.

Fourth, a new definition of the electron optical lateral aberration of the imaging system was given, and it was proposed that the lateral aberration of the imaging electron optical system is a combination of paraxial lateral chromatic aberration and geometric lateral aberration, not just geometric lateral aberration.

Fifth, it is confirmed that for both bi-electrode or multi-electrode electrostatic concentric spherical systems, and general electron optical imaging systems with electrostatic focusing, the system resolution is hinged on the 2nd order paraxial lateral chromatic aberration, which is only related to the initial potential and the initial angles of the escaped electrons, the field strength on the cathode surface and the linear magnification of the system, but not to the specific electrode structure of the system and the potential distribution on the axis. My research also confirmed that the well-known Recknagel-Арцимович (R – A) expression for the resolution of imaging electron optical systems generally holds.

Sixth, the circle of least confusion formed by the electron beam in the imaging system and the determination of the position of the ideal imaging plane were investigated, and the envelope of the electron rays formed by the imaging segment was vividly displayed, and so on and so forth.

The above was the gains and contributions of my research on the imaging electron optics of the concentric spherical system with electrostatic focusing. For the details of this study, readers can refer to items [1] – [5] in the literature if you are interested.

Here, I would like to share some anecdotes about imaging electron optics research. In 1955, when Soviet Union expert Dr. Семан О. И gave a lecture on electron optics at Peking University, he summed up the work of Germany's scholar A. Recknagel and Soviet Union scholar Л. А. Арцимович, and proposed a formula for evaluating the image quality in an imaging ectron-optical system (ie, cathode lens), which is called the Reckngel-Apunstosry formula, or R – A formula for short, is a major contribution of Dr. Семан О. И to the theory of imaging electron optics. Although the R – A formula was called central aberration at that time and determined the resolution capability or the resolution power of the electron optical system, its importance to the theoretical study of imaging electron optics was not really understood by the electron optics academic community at that time.

When Dr. Семан О. И was studying the cathode lens, that is, the imaging electron optical system, he found that in previous studies, the escaped electron beams were in different imaging planes. The radius of the scattering circle formed on the limit image plane, the optimal image plane and the Gaussian image plane has the following relationship:

$$\Delta r_t^* : \Delta r_m^* : \Delta r_g^* = 1 : 0.6 : 2$$

where 1 is the contribution of German A. Recknagel (1941) and British P. Schagen (1952); 0.6 is that of the Soviet Union Арцинмович (1944); 2 is that of Семан himself (1955), a Soviet Union expert who came to China to spread the theory of electron optics in the 1950s, summed up the results of Recknagel and Арцинмович, and put forward an R – A formula, which is very concise and can be expressed in the following form:

$$\Delta r = \frac{2M}{E_c} \sqrt{\varepsilon_r} (\sqrt{\varepsilon_z} - \sqrt{\varepsilon_{z1}})$$

where Δr is the second-order paraxial lateral aberration; ε_r, ε_z corresponds to the radial and axial initial energy of the escaped electron; ε_{z1} is the axial initial energy of an escaped electron corresponding to the ideal imaging position; E_c is the electric field strength at the cathode surface taking a negative value; M is the lateral magnifiation of the system. Δr is called the second order paraxial lateral chromatic aberration, which I named it to make it clear that this is due to the difference in paraxial trajectories of different axial initial energies of electrons.

This formula is very concise and very useful. It shows that the resolution of the system determined by the second-order lateral chromatic aberration of the imaging electron optical system has nothing to do with the specific structure of the system, but is only related to the field strength E_c at the cathode surface and the system magnification M and the initial energy of electron emission ε_0. The formula is of great significance for studying the theory of imaging electron optics and for guiding the design of devices, because the designer does not need to pay much attention to the structure of the device, but only needs to consider how to make the field strength of the cathode surface reach the maximum requirement, which is Семан's greatest contribution. However, it has not been proved practically. My contribution is to actually get the conclusions of Семан's research from the model of electrostatic focusing concentric spherical system and the combined electromagnetic focusing concentric spherical system.

In April 1966, when my PhD dissertation was completed, two electron optics experts should be invited, to write comments, one was Prof. П. П. Касьянков, and the other was Dr. Семан. When I saw Prof. П. П. Касьянков, he said, "Why don't you come to cooperate with me in my teaching and research department?" I said, "When I arrived at the Leningrad Electrical Technical Institute (LETI), you left, how could I ask you to be my instructor ! Now that I've graduated, you're back. I am really sorry for it. " When I went to Dr. Семан's home to get the review comments, I found that he read my paper very carefully. He took out a large stack of white paper, on which he commented on almost every chapter of my paper, full of OK! Great! Very Great! Great fellow! The old man hugged me warmly, and I was overwhelmed by his enthusiasm. When I defended my dissertation for my PhD degree in physics and mathematics in the Soviet Union, he attended the defense meeting as a dissertation reviewer. He did not criticize the shortcomings of the thesis, but praised it. So much that he suggested to LETI to keep me and study for a decade in the Soviet Union. Under the situation that Sino-Soviet relations are almost on the verge of breaking, this was of course impossible, and I did not want to.

When I went to study in Leningrnd in the early 1960s, I knew from some rumors that when Dr. Семан returned to the Soviet Union after lecturing in China, he had been frustrated and depressed a lot and he had never been awarded a senior professional title at the professor level. Of course, the reasons, right and wrong, are beyond me. I deeply feel that the Russian academic circles in the 1950s and 1960s were about factions, and the struggle between factions was quite fierce. I remember the time when the two schools of electron optics were arguing over a scientific question.

But what I hold for Dr. Семан is that the academic contribution of Russian academia to Dr. Семан's electron optics, especially some well-known electron optics academic monographs, is such an important contribution to Семан's summary of the R – A formula for determining the resolution capability of imaging devices, has fallen on deaf cars in Russian literature, not even mentioned. When he returned to his motherland from China, regardless of his academic contributions and academic status, he was suppressed all the time, which I deeply feel sorry for him.

Today, when I look back on the research and exploration on imaging electron optics during my studies in Leningrad, I found myself virtually overwhelmed with countless emotions. If I hadn't been so dedicated to research at that time, or if I were afraid for the difficulties, I could have looked for all kinds of excuses and retired with a high-sounding appearance. However, excuses or reasons simply never occurred to me. I thought I wanted to forge ahead, since " there aren't many opportunities worth fighting for in one's life. " That's right! Success or failure, I must always be worthy of my parents and fellow villagers!

During the days and nights of my application to science in the Shedlin Library in Leningrad, I took a nap when exhausted, drank cold water when thirsty, and ate a piece of bread when hungry. In the exploration of each question, I made a lot of reading notes and literature cards, and got the answer after smearing countless scratch papers. No one knew my hardships; I was the only one aware of them. My three and a half years of stay in Leningrad was considered by many people to be too hard, too lonely, and too difficult. However, I have always liked to explore the unknown, and I feel joy in hard work. Sometimes I missed my family and relatives very much. Once I made some discovery in scientific exploration, I felt like the happiest person in the world.

I clearly remember that one night when I was studying at the Shedlin Library in Leningrad, I probably dozed off without knowing it, because I had been so tired. I had no idea how many hours had passed, and it was already midnight when the waiter woke me up. I hurriedly put on my coat and ran to the station. In Leningrad winter, the climate can be very cold and windy. The tram never came, and I was cold and anxious, stomping my feet. At that time, there was no taxi profession in Leningrad, and there were few private cars. I thought to myself, if the tram was never to show up, in this cold weather, I would freeze to death on the streets of Leningrad tonight. Fortunately, a tram came slowly. I was overjoyed, hopped on the tram and returned to my dorm. I was so lucky.

The experience of studying in the Soviet Union is a valuable asset in my life. During my stay in the Soviet Union, I went through a difficult scientific journey and established a strong belief and confidence in my academic life. After entering the 1990s, I tried my best to communicate the friendly exchanges between China and Russia in the field of electron optics, and tried my best to promote academic exchanges and cooperation between the two countries.

III. Research on Imaging Electron Optics of Concentric Spherical System with Combined Electromagnetic Focusing

In May 1966, I returned home from the Soviet Union. In April 1968, because of domestic political movement, I fled to Shanghai and I felt that I couldn't just follow the crowd, and I should make conscious efforts to enhance my scientific research. Therefore, I went to the Shanghai library to read and study every day, while translating my PhD dissertation in physics and mathematics accomplished in the Soviet Union.

One day, it occurred to me that the set of theories on the electron optics of the concentric spherical system with electrostatic focusing that I had studied in Leningrad, the Soviet Union, might be extended to the electron optics of the concentric spherical system with combined electromagnetic focusing. It was something that had not been studied before, and would be of theoretical and practical significance. So, I started my exploration in Shanghai. I was busy from morning to night, but mostly in vain. But, it had to be the way. In spring of 1971, I went to Zhumadian city, Henan Province, and then to the "May 7th Cadre School" of Beijing Institute of Technology in Daxing County, Beijing, to work and accept thought remolding labor reform for a year. During this period, I worked in the production team of the village of Tangfangzhuang, Zhumadian city, Henan Province, for three months, eating, living, and working with farmers.

After I returned from the "May 7th Cadre School" in the spring of 1972, I served as the nominal head of a teaching and research section of night vision technology, taking charge of its daily work. When the students of 1972 class officially began to study night vision technology, I became busy arranging their syllabus, giving them lessons, and then leading them to the state-run Yunnan Optical Instrument Factory in city Kunming, Yunnan province for an internship. Between my roles, I found myself constantly thinking about new scientific problems in imaging electron optics, despite my hectic schedule. The research went on and off, but I never gave up. Fortunately, my research at that time required only a pen and a piece of paper. In early 1975, I completed and translated the first draft of a research thesis on electron optics of concentric spherical systems with combined electromagnetic focusing into English. Here, I'll briefly talk about the thinking and process of this research topic.

I have always called myself a trekker in the scientific realm, a scientific man constantly on the path of exploration. Just like Newton had said, I am also a child full of joy searching for beautiful shells by the sea, jumping up delightfully for every bright and colorful shell found. In the following section, I will focus on the electron optics of the concentric spherical system with combined electromagnetic focusing, as well as the extension from static imaging electron optics to dynamic imaging electron optics, to how I found those beautiful shells in imaging electron optics!

In the field of imaging electron optics, the electron optics of electrostatic proximity focusing systems, electrostatic focusing concentric spherical systems, uniform parallel combined electromagnetic focusing systems, and combined electromagnetic focusing concentric spherical systems had been separately studied and those imaging systems have some common properties, specifically the same geometric structure and simple electromagnetic configuration. Obviously, if the magnetic field disappears or the spherical radius becomes infinite, the concentric spherical system with combined electromagnetic focusing becomes an electrostatic focusing concentric spherical system or a parallel uniform electromagnetic focusing system, and the former becomes a proximity electrostatic focusing system. During my stay in the Soviet Union, I initially solved some scientific problems of electron optics of electrostatic focusing concentric spherical system. In April 1968, when I studied in the Shanghai library I suddenly thought of whether I could extend my scientific research in Russia to the field of electromagnetic focusing and make some contributions to the theory of imaging electron optics, which could be a work of scientific significance. What I pondered was whether the electron trajectories of the concentric spherical system with combined electromagnetic focusing could be expressed by a unified universal analytical solution. If two special solutions of the paraxial equation could be obtained, just like the concentric spherical system with electrostatic focusing, all problems of its electron optical imaging characteristics and lateral aberration could be solved easily. However, in the electron trajectory equation, there are both electrical parameters, magnetic parameters, geometric parameters, and initial velocity parameters of the escaped electron axis, it was by no means easy to find an analytical solution. This tricky issue naturally became the focus of my concern, but I had not been able to obtain satisfactory results.

Of course, the paraxial equation of electron optics is a second-order linear homogeneous differential equation, and it is not difficult to obtain its electron trajectory numerically by computer. However, its disadvantage was its insufficiency to analyze its results to study its underlying physical properties. Fortunately, when I was studying in the Soviet Union in the early 1960s, I had a relatively in-depth study on the electron optics of the bi-electrode concentric spherical system with electrostatic focusing and the parallel uniform electromagnetic focusing system, which gave me the reference and incentive to study the electron optics of concentric spherical system with electromagnetic focusing.

I had been thinking about the solution of the electron motion in the electromagnetically focused concentric spherical system. I felt that it should be the same as the electrostatically focused concentric spherical system, and therefore it must be able to obtain the analytical solution of the electron motion equation. However, I just couldn't figure it out. I remember one night in the early 1970s when I was lying in bed, thinking about this problem, I dozed off. Then suddenly an idea came to me, like a dream. It flashed across my mind and I woke up with a start. The solution was exactly the solution I had been thinking about. I quickly got out of bed and wrote it down… In fact, the analytical solution obtained by me back then was based on the method of "analogy." Instead of directly tackling the differential equation, I compared the combined electromagnetic concentric spherical system with the known special solution of the parallel uniform system with electromagnetic focusing, and introduced geometric parameters $n = R_c/R_a$ (R_c, R_a are the curvature radii of the spherical cathode and spherical anode of the concentric spherical system, respectively). By using the Wronski determinant, I derived the two special solutions of the concentric spherical system with combined electromagnetic focusing and the analytical expression of its electron rotation angle. When the spherical radius of cathode and anode extends to infinity, that is, when $n = 1$, it becomes the solution of the uniform parallel electromagnetic focusing system, and when the magnetic field disappears, that is, when the magnetic induction intensity $B = 0$, it becomes the solution of the bi-electrode concentric spherical system with electrostatic focusing. I presented the results of my research at the 1978 International Conference on Photoelectronic Imaging Devices in London, and my paper "Electron Optics of Concentric Spherical Electromagnetic Focusing Systems" was included in *Advances in Electronics and Electron Physics* published in 1979, Volume 52, page 119 – 132. Although the analytical solution of the trajectory in this paper was not strictly derived by differential equations, but by analogy, it is correct because it satisfies the paraxial equation of electron optics. By the way, literature shows that at about the same time in 1979, a group of Russian scholars on electron optics at the Siberian branch of the USSR Academy of Sciences were also working on this problem. However, they did not obtain an accurate analytical solution of the electron travel trajectories in the combined electromagnetic focusing concentric spherical system. Instead, they obtained only the zero-order approximate solution.

When I studied this problem once again, I directly began with solving the second-order linear homogeneous differential equation, to rigorously deduce the analytical solutions of the two special solutions of the paraxial equation of electron optics. My work shows that the analytical solution of the trajectory in the concentric spherical system with combined electromagnetic focusing can be directly obtained from the paraxial equation of electron optics, that is, the second-order homogeneous linear differential equation, including exact solution, paraxial solution, approximate solution and asymptotic solution, and the paraxial lateral aberration of the system. I proved that the R – A formula was still valid in the combined electromagnetic imaging system, taking the three systems of electrostatic focusing concentric spherical system, uniform parallel combined electromagnetic system and electrostatic proximity focusing system as special cases of this system. It should be pointed out that in April 2019, the two-special solutions of the paraxial equations that I published in English in the Chinese journal *Acta Optica Sinica*, were all obtained by rigorously solving second-order homogeneous linear differential equations. The argumentation was much better than it was forty years ago. In April 2022, I compiled 4 articles for publication in the 8th issue of *Acta Optica Sinica*, in April, including "Imaging Electron Optics of Electrostatically Focused Concentric Spherical Systems." My article shows that, whether for both the electrostatic concentric spherical system and the electromagnetic combined concentric spherical system, I could obtain the analytical expression of its special solution, which had never been obtained before. Likewise, I also proved that the composition of lateral aberrations I proposed above still holds in the electron optics of the combined electromagnetic concentric spherical system.

It should be pointed out that the article I presented at the International Conference on Photoelectronic Imaging Devices in London, Great Britain in 1978 and published in the US publication *Advances in Electronics and Electron Physics* in 1979 was published virtually at the same as the three Russian scientists Смирнов Н. А, Monastyrski (Монастерский М. А) and Куликов Ю. В in 1979 in *Журнал Технической Физики* (*Journal of Technical Physics*), a journal of the USSR Academy of Sciences. Mine was published in 1978, and theirs was published in 1979. Both were discussing the same issues—electron optics for concentric spherical systems with combined electromagnetic focusing (Fig. 3), and we both did it independently.

So, what is the difference between me and the Russian scholars in the research on imaging electron optics? I will briefly talk about it. We were studying the same electron optics problem—in short, it means solving the following electron optics paraxial equation in a combined electromagnetic concentric spherical system:

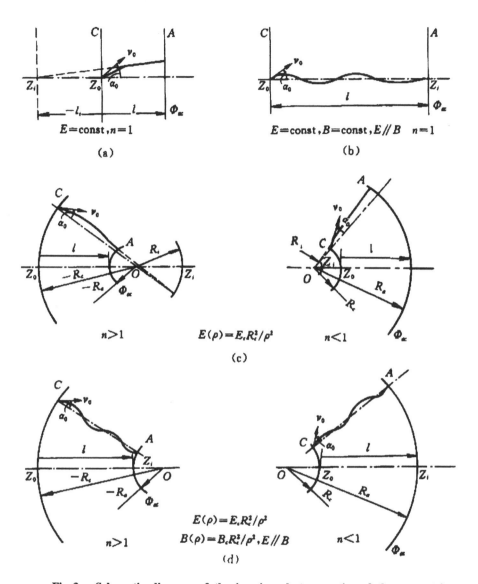

Fig. 3   Schematic diagram of the imaging electron optics of the concentric spherical system with electromagnetic focusing

$$u^{*\prime\prime}(z) + \frac{\phi'(z)}{2[\phi(z) + \varepsilon_z]} u^{*\prime}(z) + \frac{1}{4[\phi(z) + \varepsilon_z]}$$

$$\times \left\{ \phi''(z) + \frac{e}{2m_0}B^2(z) \right\} u^*(z) = 0$$

where $u^*(z)$ represents the paraxial electron trajectory in the rotating coordinate system; $\phi(z)$ and $B(z)$ represents the potential distribution and magnetic induction distribution on the axis, respectively; e/m_0 represents the electron charge-to-mass ratio; and ε_z is the axial initial potential corresponding to the initial energy of the escaped electrons.

It can be seen that both of us wanted to find two special solutions of the above the second-order homogeneous linear differential equation in the combined electromagnetic concentric spherical system, but the equation contained not only geometric parameters and electrical parameters, but also ε_z, representing the small amount of initial axis energy of the escaped electrons. That made the solution very difficult. For this reason, the three Russian scientists ignored this tiny quantity ε_z and regarded it as a perturbation to the differential equation and considered it in dealing with aberrations. Because of this treatment, they did not consider the change of the axial initial energy of the escaped electrons in their study, that is, they assumed that the axial initial energy of the escaped electrons $\varepsilon_z = 0$. This of course greatly simplified the solution of the differential equation, but their theories based on this assumption was naturally flawed.

The theory we studied was based on the assumption that the axial initial energy of the escaped electron $\varepsilon_z \neq 0$, so was the entire solution or calculation accordingly. The tiny quantity of ε_z in the above differential equation was not discarded. On this basis, I obtained $v(z,\varepsilon_z)$ and $w(z, \varepsilon_z)$ the two special solutions of the above paraxial equations of the combined electromagnetic concentric spherical imaging system, as well as the analytical expression of their rotation angle $\chi(z,\varepsilon_z)$, as follows:

$$v(z,\varepsilon_z) = \frac{2z\sqrt{-E_c}}{k\phi(z)} \sin\left\{\frac{k}{\sqrt{-E_c}}[\sqrt{\phi(z) + \varepsilon_z} - \sqrt{\varepsilon_z}]\right\}$$

$$w(z,\varepsilon_z) = (1 + \frac{z}{R_c}) \cos\left\{\frac{k}{\sqrt{-E_c}}[\sqrt{\phi(z) + \varepsilon_z} - \sqrt{\varepsilon_z}]\right\}$$

$$-\frac{\sqrt{\varepsilon_z}}{R_c}\frac{2z}{k\phi(z)}\sin\left\{\frac{k}{\sqrt{-E_c}}\left[\sqrt{\phi(z)+\varepsilon_z}-\sqrt{\varepsilon_z}\right]\right\}$$

$$\chi(z,\varepsilon_z)=\frac{k}{\sqrt{-E_c}}\left\{\sqrt{\phi(z)+\varepsilon_z}-\sqrt{\varepsilon_z}\right\}$$

where E_c and B_0 are the electric field intensity and magnetic induction intensity on the cathode surface respectively; $k^2=\dfrac{e}{2m_0}\dfrac{B_0^2}{-E_c}$; R_c is the radius of curvature of the spherical cathode of the concentric spherical system, and e/m_0, the electron charge-to-mass ratio.

Assuming that the axial initial energy $\varepsilon_z=0$, the expression of the above-mentioned special solution $v(z)$, $w(z)$ and the rotation angle $\chi(z)$ can be simplified as

$$v(z)=\frac{2z\sqrt{-E_c}}{k\phi(z)}\sin\left\{\frac{k}{\sqrt{-E_c}}\sqrt{\phi(z)}\right\}$$

$$w(z)=(1+\frac{z}{R_c})\cos\left\{\frac{k}{\sqrt{-E_c}}\sqrt{\phi(z)}\right\}$$

$$\chi(z)=\frac{k}{\sqrt{-E_c}}\sqrt{\phi(z)}$$

This is exactly the expression given by three Russian scientists Смирнов Н. А, Монастерский М. А, Куликов Ю. В in 1979, published in the Soviet Union's *Журнал Технической Физики* (*Journal of Technical Physics*), in Volume 48, No. 2, page 2590 – 2595. The thesis was titled " Некоторые вопросы электронной оптики катодных линз с кобинированными полями, обладающими сферической симметриией" ("Research on Several Issues of the Electron Optics of Cathode Lens with Spherically Symmetric Field"). It can be seen from that in studying the electron optics of the combined electromagnetic concentric spherical system, their differential equation did not consider the axial initial energy ε_z in finding the trajectory solution, and yielded the zero-order approximate solution of the paraxial trajectory, which is a special case of our above result. The analytical solution of the electrostatic and combined electromagnetic concentric spherical system that I have given above corrects the mistakes of some Russian and Western scholars, remedies their deficiencies, advances the theory and method of imaging electron optics and contributes to the theoretical treasure trove of imaging electron optics.

That is the difference between me and Russian scholars in studying the theory of imaging electron optics. Such differences are reflected in practice. In designing the electron optical system for computational imaging, Russian scientists set the image plane at the drop point of the trajectory of $\varepsilon_{z1} = 0$, which is the so-called limiting image plane. By the way, in some Russian literature, this image plane is often called the Gaussian image plane, and it is considered as the ideal imaging surface. In our processing, the focus is on where to set the image plane to get the best image quality, that is, to get the clearest image. Therefore, efforts must be made to choose the so-called optimal image plane, which corresponds to a certain value where $\varepsilon_{z1} \neq 0$. As I have proved above, for a bi-electrode concentric spherical system, electron beams, whether monochromatic or panchromatic, will form an electron ray envelope when it is focused and imaged, after emitting from an axial point. The place where the envelope is the most dense can be determined as the position of the best image plane, corresponding to a value somewhere in $0 \leqslant \varepsilon_{z1} \leqslant \varepsilon_{max}$. When we design the image tube, we can set the value of ε_{z1}. This is an important difference between us and Russian scholars in studying electron optics theory and designing electron optical software packages. In addition, theoretically, Russian scholars did not distinguish paraxial lateral aberration from geometric lateral aberration in giving the lateral aberration expression, but we strictly separate these two types of aberrations.

Our research shows that the paraxial lateral aberration can be composed by the paraxial lateral chromatic aberration

$$\Delta r_{v2}^* = \frac{2M}{E_c} \sqrt{\varepsilon_r} (\sqrt{\varepsilon_z} - \sqrt{\varepsilon_{z1}})$$

and the paraxial chromatic aberration of magnification

$$\Delta r_{w2}^* (z_i, \varepsilon_z) = |r_0| M \left[\frac{-k}{\sqrt{-E_c}} (\sqrt{\varepsilon_z} - \sqrt{\varepsilon_{z1}}) \right]$$

which is at the direction of $k \times r_0$,

and the paraxial anisotropic chromatic aberration

$$\Delta r_{u2}^* (z_i, \varepsilon_z) = |r_0| M \frac{k}{\sqrt{-E_c}} (\sqrt{\varepsilon_z} - \sqrt{\varepsilon_{z1}})$$

which is at the direction r_0, etc.

Therefore, either for the electrostatic focusing concentric spherical system or for the electromagnetic combined focusing concentric spherical system, the paraxial lateral chromatic aberration is determined by R – A formula.

In the early 21st century, Prof. Schelev M. Ya, director of the Photoelectron Imaging Research Section of the Institute of General Physics of the Russian Academy of Sciences, invited me to collaborate with them on electron optics for dynamic imaging. He proposed that since we were studying the same subject of imaging electron optics, which served the design and development of image tubes and image intensifiers, it might be advisable to test the imaging electron optics software packages of our two computing image intensifiers. I followed his suggestion and asked them to put forth the questions for us to calculate and compare with the results. For a certain electron optical system for high-speed photographic image intensifiers proposed by Russia, the calculation results of the ELIM (from Russia) software package and the ODESI (from China) software package were: $-1.508, 17$ and $-1.525, 80$ for the linear magnification respectively; 35.2% and 37.7% for the edge distortions respectively, and 356.344mm and 361.088mm for the image plane positions respectively. Since the Russian side took the limiting image plane position, which was closer to the cathode plane, and we took the best image plane position, which was a little bit farther away. However, the differences in calculation results of the two packages were very small, and they were very close to the actual measurement results of the device. We were all satisfied and applauded for the calculation results.

It should be pointed out that, both in the Western and Russian academic circles, the research on imaging electron optics did not strictly distinguish between paraxial lateral aberration and geometric lateral aberration. For example, my Russian counterparts in electron optics usually only cared about the lateral aberration formed on the limiting image plane, that is, when $\varepsilon_{z1} = 0$, and the lateral aberration expression did not strictly distinguish which was paraxial lateral aberration or geometric lateral aberration. However, in our study of imaging electron optics the lateral aberration on any image plane between $\varepsilon_{z1} = 0$ and $\varepsilon_{z1} = \varepsilon_{max}$ were given, and there was strict difference between paraxial and geometric lateral aberration.

Defining the lateral aberration of the imaging electron optical system as the combination of paraxial and geometric lateral aberration was the conclusion I reached after examining the difference between the paraxial trajectory and the actual trajectory of the concentric spherical system with electrostatic focusing. And the conclusion was known to hold true. Moreover, it still holds in the combined electromagnetic concentric spherical system. For decades, my assertion was never challenged by the academic community of imaging electron optics.

On September 2000, Academician Alexander M. Prokhorov, the

Nobel Prize winner and president of the Russian Federal Academy of Engineering of Sciences, said in his congratulatory letter to me on my election as a foreign member of Russian Federal Academy of Engineering Sciences that "You are the founder of your own school of science." as following:

Dear Professor Zhou Liwei:

On behalf of the Presidium of the Russian Federal Academy of Engineering Sciences, we are pleased to inform you that you have been elected as a foreign member of the Russian Federal Academy of Engineering Sciences. We know that you are a distinguished scientist, world-renowned expert, and author of numerous monographs and academic papers in the field of charged particle optics and related applications.

We always remember that you started your scientific activities at the Leningrad Electrical Technical Institute (LETI) and that you have maintained an unwavering love and respect for our country throughout your life. When you return to your home motherland, you have closely linked your whole life with Beijing Institute of Technology, where you have experienced a long and glorious journey, from an ordinary lecturer to a recognized expert, full professor, director of the Academic Committee, academician of the Chinese Academy of Engineering.

You are the founder of your own school of science. Many of your talented young people who graduated from Beijing Institute of Technology call you teacher with reverence and pride. You have been awarded numerous national awards, praise and encourage, and honorary titles for your outstanding achievements. You are undoubtedly a faithful servant of science, a son of the best in your country.

Throughout your career, you have studied the laws of motion of electron beams; like the electrons in an electron beam, you yourself are constantly in motion. It seems hard to imagine some meaningful scientific events in China without your participation.

Your warm and energetic energy, persevering optimism and kindness make you and those around you always happy and joyful, and it even surprises everyone who knows and approaches you.

On this memorable day, please accept our warmest congratulations and wish you good health, fruitful work and great new achievements in science.

Faithfully Yours.

So far, I described how I had explored imaging electron optics of concentric spherical systems with electrostatic and electromagnetic focusing, and how I had entered the hall of imaging electron optics science. After many difficulties, I finally cleared the fog and found out the truth, and established a set of theoretical systems of our own. I sincerely hope that you will not be misled to think that I am a very smart person that has effortlessly explored the mystery of the aberration of the imaging electron optical system, and ventured into the sacred temple of science. In fact, I have always felt that due to my clumsiness, my scientific research was like climbing a mountain. I had to fumble ahead step by step, and managed to reach the top after zigzag path with countless detours and untold hardships. However, I found that there had been a direct path, which required much fewer efforts. When I obtained the result with strenuous efforts only to find that it could have been so obvious and simple, I felt myself the dumbest person on the planet. Why hadn't obtained it earlier? Fortunately, I am a persevering person, refusing to give up halfway, but groping forward in difficult times.

Regarding the research on imaging electron optics, my experience was that we should learn from our predecessors but not blindly trust them, and that we should question them, but respect them. Stepping into the hall of science and exploring the mysteries within it can be highly contingent. Even a flash of inspiration is the result of long-term accumulation and hard thinking. Remember that there is more than one road to science. You just have to try. Maybe the way you find is more direct and convenient than those taken by the predecessors.

The above are my achievements and contributions in the research on imaging electron optics of concentric spherical systems with electromagnetic focusing. For further details, interested readers may refer to the literature [6] – [10].

By the way, here I would like to talk about a strange thing of this paper led me to go abroad to attend academic conferences. It really happened to me like a legend. At the beginning of 1978, our Ministry of Foreign Affairs received a letter from the British Rank Group Corporation and Imperial College London, inviting me to attend the International Conference on Photoelectronic Imaging Devices and the International Conference on Electronic Imaging held in London, the United Kingdom in September 1978, and hoped that I could participate in the conference and read a scientific paper. But I didn't know the person who invited me, it was recommended to him by someone else. Maybe, he knew that I was studying in the Soviet Union to study electron optics, and I had quoted his article. This is a very common thing now, but it was regarded as a very rare and amazing thing back then. Our Ministry of Foreign Affairs went to the Fifth Ministry of Machine Building Industry, only to know that Zhou Liwei was a teaching assistant at Beijing Institute of Technology and a PhD who returned from studying in the Soviet Union. When the relevant leaders of the Fifth Ministry of Machine Building Industry knew about this, they thought it was an excellent opportunity to learn about the progress of modern photoelectronic imaging technology abroad. At that time, General Wang Zhen, who was in charge of science and technology in the central government, ordered the Fifth Ministry of Machine Building Industry and the Ministry of Electronics Industry to form a delegation to select candidates to attend the meeting.

I did not give up scientific research during the "Cultural Revolution" period, and the imaging electron optics of the electromagnetic focusing concentric spherical system is the continuation and development of my research work in the Soviet Union. Since April 1968, when I escaped from school and returned to Shanghai to avoid fighting, I have been immersed in my research on this topic. By 1975, the Chinese version of my research paper had been written and mimeographed. When I heard the news, I thought it was definitely me who went to the UK to participate in the conference, because my research has new findings and results, and I could communicate with my foreign counterparts. However, when the leaders of the institute and department discussed the matter, there was some controversy about whether to send me to the UK to participate the conference.

After I returned from my visit to the UK, a comrade in charge of dispatching from the Fifth Ministry of Machine Building Industry said to me, "Your director Li Zhenyi of the Department is so kind to you! We were really worried at the time, we were afraid that you would run away. It was director Li who tried his best to recommend and guarantee your ticket before you left the country." It is difficult for today's people to understand the distrust and precautionary mentality between people at that time. In those days, it was normal to have nothing to do with oneself and to hang up. Director Li Zhenyi supported me in attending the meeting in the UK and was willing to serve as my guarantor, which was a political risk if something happens, he will be implicated and severely punished. But he trusted me so much that he did not hesitate to be my surety. I am very grateful to director Li. He has always been a leader and elder who cared for me. He has silently recommended and supported me from teaching at the school, studying abroad, recommending admission to the department and the school's academic committee, serving as a member of the subject evaluation group of the Academic Committee o the State Council, being promoted to full professor, and winning various honors and titles. But director Li never told me that he recommended me, guaranteed me to the leaders of the school and department, and never advertised to the outside world that he helped me and recommended me, thinking that this is what he should do. For decades, I was in Beijing Institute of Technology, and he always silently supported me. loved and helped me. It would be no exaggeration to say that he is my bole. In February of this year, he unfortunately passed away at the age of 96. He will always live in my heart. I will always learn his spirit. May he rest in peace in heaven.

It should be said that the difficulties I encountered in going abroad at that time were hard to imagine by current researchers. The first was my English, which I only learned in high school and Russian language in college. Although I can read scientific and technical literature in English, listening, speaking and writing in English were extremely difficult for me. I have always described my English as a "three legged cat" level, seemingly able to walk, but limping. The second is the printing of the English abstract and the full text of the paper, which requires specialized English typewriters and typists. In addition, the presentation of the thesis was more difficult, my pronunciation was completely Russian, before Microsoft PowerPoint (PPT) etc. , and there were no transparencies in schools. Therefore, the manuscript should be filmed first, and then made into a slideshow to show the explanation during the speech.

Fortunately, the vice principal of BIT Professor Yan Peiran helped me modify my English, and Mrs Chen Xinwu helped me with typing. Without the help of the two of them, I would not have been able to complete the writing and presentation of the manuscript. Looking back on these events today, I am deeply grateful to them. I won't go into detail here.

In the autumn of 1978, the 3rd Plenary Session of the 11th Central Committee of the Party had not yet been held, the country had not yet opened to the outside world, and the procedures for going abroad were extremely strict. Since the Beijing Institute of Technology was still kept secret, I went abroad in the name of a researcher of another corporation.

In the autumn of 1978, the 6th International Conference on Photoelectronic Imaging Devices held at Imperial College London was initiated by Prof. J. D. McGee of Imperial College London. At this conference, there were two papers on the report on electron optics, which one was presented by Associate Prof. A. Choudry from the University of Rhode Island and the other was me successively. The title of my report is "Electron Optics of Concentric Spherical Electromagnetic Focusing Systems." In my report, I expressed the solutions of the electron trajectories of the four types of electron optical systems in a unified form, obtained a universal analytical solution, and discussed the imaging characteristics and aberrations of electron optics, as well as application prospects. I didn't know how my presentation went, but it ended with a round of applause. I knew that the applause was purely polite. But I felt so relieved at the time, that I did my best, that I got the job done, and that no matter what the people in the meeting thought of me, I finally got the job done. Associate Prof. A. Choudry's report was relatively simple and casual. He roughly talked about some assumptions and ideas about the study of the proximity focusing system, but there was no clear conclusion and result.

A total of 80 papers were read out at this conference, and 40 papers were selected into the conference proceedings. My paper was selected, but associate Prof. Choudry's paper was not selected. Associate Prof. Choudry did not mind and was very friendly to me. On November 28, 1978 he wrote to me wishing to conduct scientific research cooperation on the proximity imaging of cathode lens, and invited me to visit the University of Rhode Island in the United States to have a lecture. The full text of my paper I presented at the conference was published in volume 52 of "*Advances in Electronics and Electron Physics*" in 1979, which attracted the attention of foreign electron optics counterparts, and made me a little reputation in the domestic optical and weapon circles.

The International Conference on Electronic Imaging was initiated by the Rank Organization in the United Kingdom. Dr. P. Schagen was the host of the conference. He was a famous British night vision technology expert and one of the first scholars, who started the research on imaging electron optics of electrostate focusing concentric system, because I have extended the study of electrostatic focusing concentric spherical systems to the field of electromagnetic focusing, he especially appreciated my work. At this conference, I was impressed by Dr. Schelev M. Ya from the Institute of General Physics of the USSR Academy of Sciences, who demonstrated the achievements of the USSR Academy of Sciences in the field of high-speed photographic imaging devices with a high scientific level. I have been in friendly contact with both of them since I met them at his conference. In the early 1980s, I invited Dr. P. Schagen to give lectures in our institute. In the early 21st century, director Schelev M. Ya invited me to the Institute of General Physics of the Russian Academy of Sciences in Moscow for scientific cooperation.

At the International Conference on Electronic Imaging, I asked

Dr. P. Schagen why I was invited to participate in these two conferences? He said the meeting was initiated by the Rank Organization, with the support of the Duke of Kent, the Queen's nephew. Dr. P. Schagen assured the Duke of Kent that the conference would invite scientists from the two largest countries behind the iron curtain, i. e. , the Soviet Union and China, to demonstrate the international universality and breadth of the conference. Therefore, he invited Dr. Schelev, a Soviet scientist who had studied in France, and Dr. Zhou Liwei, a Chinese scientist who had studied in the Soviet Union, to attend the meeting. Here, the so-called "behind the iron curtain" countries refer to the mysterious and unknown countries that were closed to the outside world at that time and seemed to be shrouded by the iron curtain, namely the Soviet Union and China, because these two countries were not closely related to western countries in various aspects at that time. There were very few contacts and interactions. Especially in China, the "Cultural Revolution" almost cut off academic ties with foreign countries. After I led the delegation to London, we received a warm welcome. The British side showed us its sincerity in the exchanges between scientists and people of China and the UK, and gave us a tour of the most advanced optoelectronic imaging technology at that time. After the two international conferences, the Duke of Kent held a grand reception banquet to entertain scientists from all over the world. The Duke of Kent also met with the Chinese delegation before the banquet and extended a warm welcome to me and the members of the delegation.

Because I lived up to my mission and completed my task abroad very well. In particular, my academic paper was selected by the conference proceedings, but the American associate professor's paper was not selected, and he also invited me to the United States for scientific cooperation. This is a very common thing now, but at that time, everyone thought that I had won face for the Chinese people. After I returned to China, I was praised by the Fifth Ministry of Machine Building Industry and the leaders of BIT. I was very happy that some of the people who have always tried to embarrass me were no longer bothering me.

After I returned to China after the meeting, I suggested to the Fifth Ministry of Machine Building Industry and our institute to invite Dr. P. Schagen, a British night vision technology expert, and some British photoelectronic companies to visit China. I also proposed to the corporation under the Fifth Ministry of Machine Building Industry introduce the first generation of image cathode like the suggestion of intensifiers, etc. , the initial connection of the introduction line was also pulled by me. Many comrades told me that 1978 was a year of great joy and a year of turning over for me.

I am now writing this past event to let everyone know that there is true love in the world. I am deeply grateful to the leaders, teachers and comrades who cared for me back then.

IV. Research on Imaging Electron Optics with Curvilinear Axis and its Optimization Design

Since 1978, my collaborator, the senior engineer Fang Erlun and I, as well as my graduate students Ni Guoqiang, Pan Shunchen, Ai Kecong, Jin Weiqi, and Zhang Zhiquan et al. have successfully solved some special and universal problems of static imaging electron optics, for example, electron optics of concentric spherical systems with combined electromagnetic focusing, electron optics of combined electromagnetic system for image transference, electron optics of oblique image system, electron optics of hyperbolic field focusing system, aberration theory of electromagnetic combined focusing in cathode lens, electron optical transfer function of cathode lenses, and theory and design of electron optical system with curved axis. All those studies, either in method or in theory, had unique features and new conclusions, but I wish not to burden my readers with the details here.

The study of the imaging electron optical properties and aberrations of the concentric spherical systems with electrostatic and combined electromagnetic focusing showed that the paraxial equation (either the trajectory equation or the motion equation) was effective and accurate in solving the trajectories of electrons traveling near the symmetry axis, and thus able to give the ideal imaging and central aberrations of the system. However, when the electrons escape from the off-axis point of the cathode surface, it would be very complicated to use the integral expressions of various special types of the third-order geometric lateral aberration coefficients expressed by the axial potential distribution $\phi(z)$ and axial magnetic induction distribution $B(z)$ and their derivatives to obtain a solution. More importantly, the results were quite different from the data yielded in real tests. The reason is that the spatial potential distribution and the spatial magnetic induction distribution of the system are both expressed by Scherzer series expansion, which is far from the real distribution, especially when the cathode surface is curved or spherical. Therefore, we turned to the imaging electron optics of electron beam focusing with curved axis, called imaging electron optics with curved axis or curvilinear axial electron optics for short.

In view of this, it was in the 1970s, I proposed to extend the concept of "paraxial imaging" to "off-axis imaging" to address the problem of the focusing and imaging of off-axis electron trajectories for electron optical imaging with large object surface and wide electron beam focusing. We know that the main trajectory emitted from the object point on the axis is a straight line, that is, a symmetrical axis. The trajectory around the symmetrical axis is called the "paraxial trajectory;" that emitted by the object point beyond the cathode axis is a planar or rotated curve. Therefore, we call the trajectory around this curvilinear axis as "curved paraxial trajectory," or "curved paraxial optics," and study the theory of focusing and imaging around this "curved paraxial trajectory." That is to say, the problem of large object surface and wide electron beam focusing imaging can be solved by studying the main trajectory around the curvilinear axis.

To this end, we deduced the main trajectory equation with the main trajectory as the curvilinear axis

$$r'' = \frac{1 + r'^2}{2[\varphi(z,r) + \varepsilon_s]}\left(\frac{\partial\varphi}{\partial r} - r'\frac{\partial\varphi}{\partial z}\right)$$

as well as the meridional trajectory equation and the sagittal trajectory equation moving around the main trajectory.

$$p_2'' + F_1 p_2' + F_2 p_2 = 0$$

$$p_3'' + G_1 p_3' + G_2 p_3 = 0$$

where $F_1 = G_1 = \dfrac{1 + r'^2}{2[\varphi(z,r) + \varepsilon_s]} \dfrac{\partial \varphi}{\partial z}$

$$F_2 = \frac{3r''^2}{(1 + r'^2)^2} + \frac{1}{2[\varphi(z,r) + \varepsilon_s]}\left(-\frac{\partial^2 \varphi}{\partial r^2} + 2r'\frac{\partial^2 \varphi}{\partial r \partial z} - r'^2\frac{\partial^2 \varphi}{\partial z^2}\right)$$

$$G_2 = -\frac{1 + r'^2}{2[\varphi(z,r) + \varepsilon_s]} \frac{1}{r} \frac{\partial \varphi}{\partial r}$$

The meridional and sagittal trajectories were calculated by using the data of the electrostatic potential distribution and the magnetic induction distribution on the main trajectory of the curvilinear axis in the electron travelling path. Such an assumption is far more accurate than the Scherzer series expansion of the axial potential distribution, and much more convenient and intuitive. However, the theory of electron beam focusing and imaging with large object surface and wide electron beam with off-axis involves the Frenet rotating coordinate system, which must be solved with differential geometry, tensor analysis or other mathematical methods, and must be put into practice in the software package for system design of imaging electron optics. In the 1980s, through my joint research with Fang Erlun, Ni Guoqiang and Jin Weiqi, the method of tensor analysis was used to study the motion of electrons in the rotating curvilinear coordinate system, thus establishing a relatively complete theoretical system of beam focusing and imaging on a more general basis. The problem of imaging of curvilinear axis for electron beam focusing was solved theoretically and practically. In addition, Ni Guoqiang, Fang Erlun and I jointly proposed the study of the modulation transfer function (MTF) and the point spread function (PSF) of the photoelectron imaging system with three-dimensional coordinates, as a major innovation in method. In this regard, I have not yet seen a more creative and comprehensive research article on this topic than ours.

In short, we have proposed via research that in static imaging electron optics, whether it is an imaging system with electrostatic focusing or combined electromagnetic focusing, the lateral aberration should be composed of paraxial and geometric lateral aberrations. The former is usually composed of (2nd order + 3rd order) paraxial lateral chromatic aberration, 3rd order paraxial magnification chromatic aberration, and 3rd order paraxial anisotropic coma. The latter usually consists of the 3rd order geometric lateral aberration of electron optics, such as spherical aberration, astigmatism, field curvature, coma, distortion, and etc. In this way, the composition of the lateral aberration of the imaging electron optical system has been clarified.

It should be pointed out that Fang Erlun, I and my graduate students studied imaging electron optics to explore the basic theories and laws of electron optical imaging, to study the theory of wide electron beam focusing with curvilinear axis, and to do our bit to the treasure house of electron optics theory on the one hand; on the other hand, our research was not illusory or detached from reality. We applied our theory to the calculation and design for night vision image intensifiers. In 1978, the calculation and design for the electron optical system of the image converter tube and the image intensifier jointly developed by Fang Erlun, Feng Chitao and I won the National Science Conference Award. In the 1980s, Fang Erlun and I continued to cooperate in research. We used a personal computer (PC) to design the electron optical system and developed a relatively complete software package for electron optical system design in image tubes after repeated corrections and complementation, greatly promoting its popularization and application. The project "Theory and Design of Wide Electron Beam Focusing" chaired by Fang Erlun and me won the first prize of the Science and Technology Progress Award of China North Industries Corporation in 1990, and the second prize of the National Science and Technology Progress Award in 1991. In the 1990s, I cooperated with Fang Erlun, Zhang Zhiquan, Jin Weiqi, and Ni Guoqiang, to study the iterative calculation of the accelerated field using the multi-grid method. We carried out system optimization and developed "Imaging Tube Design and ODESI Software Package," which won the third prize of the National Science and Technology Progress Award in 1995. The software package has been proven highly effective after use by relevant domestic research institutes and factories. The research paved the way for China's low-light-level night vision industry from imitation to independent design and development of new night vision devices. For example, Kunming Branch of Northern Night Vision Group and Xi'an Institute of Applied Optics applied the ODESI – V electron optical system optimization design software package to design and develop the electron optics of the first-and second-generation low-light-level image tubes, and achieved significant economic benefits and social benefits. In the early 21st century, Fang Erlun, Li Yuan, and I worked together to integrate dynamic electron optical temporal aberration calculation into the design of static-imaging electron optical system, and developed the ODESI – SD software package.

So much for our achievements and contributions in studying the theory of electron optics with wide electron beam focusing and imaging. Interested readers may refer to the literature [11] – [14].

Here, I would like to point out that, as mentioned above, the theoretical research on the imaging electron optics of the electrostatic focusing concentric spherical system was completed by myself as a graduate student in Russia, and I passed the PhD degree defense of the

Soviet Union in April 1966; The theoretical research on the imaging electron optics of concentric spherical system with combined electromagnetic focusing was completed by myself during the period of " Cultural Revolution. " In 1978, the paper was published at the International Conference on Photoelectronic Imaging Devices in the United Kingdom. The research on imaging electron optics with curvilinear axis of wide electron beam focusing theory and its Optimization Design is the collective contribution of the research group led by me. The most important contribution is undoubtedly due to the senior engineer Fang Erlun. All the programs and calculations were completed by him alone. It was a pity that he became ill from overwork and unfortunately died at the age of 73. I miss him deeply.

V. Research on the Theory of Electron Optics for Dynamic Imaging

In the early 21st century, I was invited to visit the Institute of General Physics of the Russian Academy of Sciences. Prof. Schelev M. Ya, director of the Photoelectronics Department of the Institute, invited me to collaborate on the temporal aberration theory of dynamic electron optics, which was proposed for the study of ultrafast phenomena, design and calculation of high-speed photographic camera tubes. Back in 1980, Monastyrski M. A and Schelev M. Ya jointly studied and proposed the "τ Variation Temporal Aberration Theory" to calculate the temporal aberration of dynamic electron optical systems. Back in China, my affiliated unit had not asked me to study ultra-fast phenomena, so when they invited me to help them to solve scientific problems in this area, which was new for me, I was willing to have a try.

Dr. Monastyrski M. A told me that after the "τ Variation Temporal Aberration Theory" was proposed, they had tested it with a simple model, and there seemed to be no problem. However, because a simple model was used, they had always questioned the authenticity and accuracy of this theory. He told me that the term dynamic electron optics was also coined by him and Prof. Schelev M. Ya to study the time-of-flight dispersion of electrons escaping from the photocathode in a device. The two of them invited me to visit, hoping to cooperate with me to help address the truthfulness and accuracy of the "τ Variation Temporal Aberration Theory." I was very happy and willing to cooperate scientifically with them. At that time, I felt that the term "Dynamic Electron Optics" was very appropriate to the theory of temporal aberration, since it echoes the theory of spatial aberration in the study of static electron optics and is thus theoretically related to the latter.

When I took over this scientific problem, my intuition was that the static and dynamic problems of imaging electron optics should not be studied separately, as they were closely related. Obviously, when an electron escapes from the cathode surface of an electron optical imaging device, its flight trajectory is $(x,y,z;t)$, and what it carries is the space and time information, while the space-time coordinate at which it reaches the image plane is $(x_i,y_i;t_i)$. If it is used as a measurement standard, then its difference from the space-time coordinates $(x_m,y_m;t_m)$ of other electrons arriving at the image plane z_i is the spatial aberration and temporal aberration. The inter-connection between them is inevitable.

For imaging electron optics, the static optics (studying the space trajectory of electron flight) and the dynamic optics (studying the time trajectory of electron flight) are just different manifestations of the same thing, that is, the difference of the initial energy dispersion of photoelectron that escape from photocathode expressed by the spatial and temporal characteristics in the system. Therefore, it is inevitable that they have a close relationship. As shown in Fig. 4, the trajectory of the electrons reaching the image plane is represented by the spatial axis and the temporal axis, that is very clear. Therefore, since we can start from Newton's equation and Lorentz force to study the space trajectory of electron motion, we can also use it to study the time trajectory of electron motion.

My question at that time was that why Monastyrski M. A and Schelev M. Ya did not follow the usual physical approach to study the theory of temporal aberrations, that is, solving the problem by Lorentz

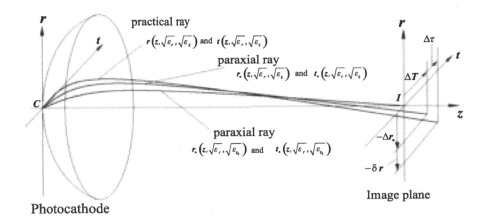

practical ray
$r\left(z,\sqrt{\varepsilon_r},\sqrt{\varepsilon_t}\right)$ and $t\left(z,\sqrt{\varepsilon_r},\sqrt{\varepsilon_t}\right)$

paraxial ray
$r_*\left(z,\sqrt{\varepsilon_r},\sqrt{\varepsilon_t}\right)$ and $t_*\left(z,\sqrt{\varepsilon_r},\sqrt{\varepsilon_t}\right)$

paraxial ray
$r_*\left(z,\sqrt{\varepsilon_r},\sqrt{\varepsilon_{t_*}}\right)$ and $t_*\left(z,\sqrt{\varepsilon_r},\sqrt{\varepsilon_{t_*}}\right)$

Image plane

Photocathode

Fig. 4　Schematic diagram of spatial and temporal aberrations formed on the image plane by electron trajectories escaping from the photocathode

force and electron motion equation. That is the fundamental way to study the electron optical properties of devices, because the Newton's motion equation already contain time variables. Why would they take the more complicated variation approach? Can I find a simpler way to study the theory of temporal aberrations? Therefore, I had to clarity and answer two questions: one is the correctness (true or false) of the "τ Variation Temporal Aberration Theory;" the other is its accuracy (precision). The first question was actually intended for testing the theory, to deny or confirm it, or to find a better replacement; the second question was to test its validity and applicability.

Therefore, I needed to study in detail the "τ Variation Temporal Aberration Theory" proposed by Russian scientists, its starting point and the process of formula derivation, and check whether there were problems in its mathematical derivation. When I translated their articles into Chinese, I studied each step of the derivation process in detail until the various expressions of the temporal aberration coefficients were obtained. In addition, in order for my graduate students to study the theory proposed by Russian scientists, I spent several days explaining it to them in detail. Since the Russian scientists limited their theory to the case of limiting image plane, I also needed to generalize it to the case of arbitrary image plane.

Our research started directly from the Lorentz force and the electron equation of motion. Sure enough, there came a difficulty in the double integral that could not be solved because of the third order derivative of the axial potential distribution appears. However, we used the properties of the electron equation of motion and the Wronski determinant itself, subtly resolved this difficulty, and obtained two lemmas for the geometric relationship and time relationship of imaging properties of the electron optics with wide beam focusing, and bypassed the complex τ variation transformation adopted by Russian scientists. A method named "Direct Integration Method for Temporal Aberration Theory" was proposed by us. It puts forth a new definition of temporal aberration, which should be the same as spatial aberration, that is, it should be composed of paraxial and geometric temporal aberration.

The total temporal aberration can be expressed by

$$\Delta t = a_2(\varepsilon_z^{1/2} - \varepsilon_{z1}^{1/2}) + A_{22}(\varepsilon_z - \varepsilon_{z1}) + A_{11}\varepsilon_r + 2A_{13}\varepsilon_r^{1/2}r_0 + A_{33}r_0^2$$

where

$$a_2 = t_{\alpha_2} = \frac{\partial t}{\partial \alpha_2} = \frac{\partial z}{\partial \alpha_2}\frac{1}{\frac{\partial z}{\partial t}} = \frac{-z_{\alpha_2}}{\dot{z}} = \frac{-\frac{2}{\phi_0'}\sqrt{\phi_*}}{\sqrt{\frac{2e}{m_0}\phi_*}}$$

$$= -\frac{1}{\phi_0'}\sqrt{\frac{2m_0}{e}} = \frac{1}{E_c}\sqrt{\frac{2m_0}{e}}$$

$$A_{22} = \frac{1}{4}\sqrt{\frac{2m_0}{e}}\frac{1}{\sqrt{\phi_*}}\left\{\frac{2}{\phi'} + 2\sqrt{\phi_*}\int_0^z \frac{\phi''}{\sqrt{\phi_*}\phi_0'^2}dz\right\}$$

$$A_{11} = \frac{1}{4}\sqrt{\frac{2m_0}{e}}\int_0^z \frac{1}{[\phi(z) + \varepsilon_z]^{3/2}}\left[-(v'^2\phi_* + \frac{1}{4}\phi''v^2) - 1\right]dz$$

$$A_{13} = \frac{1}{4}\sqrt{\frac{2m_0}{e}}\int_0^z \frac{1}{[\phi(z) + \varepsilon_z]^{3/2}}\cos(\theta_0 - \beta_0)\left(v'w'\phi_* + \frac{1}{4}\phi''vw\right)dz$$

$$A_{33} = \frac{1}{4}\sqrt{\frac{2m_0}{e}}\int_0^z \frac{1}{[\phi(z) + \varepsilon_z]^{3/2}}\left[w'^2\phi_* + \frac{1}{4}\phi''w^2 - \frac{1}{4}\phi'_0\right]dz$$

where a_2, A_{22} are coefficients of paraxial temporal chromatic aberration of the first order and second order, respectively; A_{11} is the coefficient of geometrical temporal spherical aberration of the second order; A_{13} is the coefficient of geometrical temporal field curvature aberration of the second order; A_{33} is the coefficient of geometrical temporal distortion aberration of the second order.

Thus, the total temporal aberration can be defined as:

The temporal aberration = the paraxial temporal aberration +
the geometric temporal aberration

and

The paraxial temporal aberration = 1st order paraxial temporal chromatic
aberration + 2nd order paraxial
temporal chromatic aberration + $\cdots$

The geometric temporal aberration = 2nd geometric temporal aberration(spherical aberration, field curvature, distortion) +...

Therefore, The total temporal aberration = 1st order paraxial temporal chromatic aberration + 2nd order paraxial temporal chromatic aberration + 2nd order geometric temporal aberration +...

When the bi-electrode electrostatic concentric spherical system was used for evaluation, the integral values a_2 and A_{22} of the 1st and 2nd order paraxial temporal chromatic aberration coefficients, and A_{11}, the second-order time spherical aberration coefficient obtained by the "direct integration method" were exactly the same as the analytical values. The results at the anode location were also in perfect agreement. Our work proves the correctness of using the "Direct Integration Method" for calculating temporal aberration coefficients.

By far, the current situation was that two theories had been proposed to discuss the temporal aberration, namely the "τ Variation Method" theory and the "Direct Integration Method" theory. The question of their validity had not been resolved, so it was necessary to find a way for a rigorous test. That step was intended to eliminate errors in the "deductive test" proposed by prof. Popper, a British philosopher on scientific method. We found an ideal model of a bi-electrode concentric spherical system with electrostatic focusing, and an analytical solution for the travel time of electrons in the system. The test results showed that the two theories were not only "correct" but also "exact." Being "correct" means that completely consistent results were obtained from two different approaches, and the temporal aberration coefficient expressed in the differential form in the "τ Variation Method" theory could also be expressed in integral form with "Direct Integration Method" after appropriate transformation. Being "exact" means that the calculating results of the two approaches were exact and consistent with the analytical solution of the ideal model. Finally, we also proved that the results of the "τ Variation Method" theory can also be expressed with "Direct integration method" theory after transformation.

The research showed that the "τ Variation Method" theory proposed by the Russian side and the "Direct Integration Method" theory proposed by the Chinese side are two completely different ways to effectively solve the temporal aberration theory. Russian side and Chinese side started from different angles and adopted different methods, but they both effectively solved the same problem. The "Direct Integration Method" theory had a clear concept, went straight to the subject, and was easy to solve. the " τ Variation Method" theory was novel in theory, clever in conception, and unique in thinking. Both were of great significance to promote the research of dynamic imaging electron optics. It should be pointed out that both of them were original and also reflective of the uniqueness of scientific discoveries (that is, different paths lead to the same answer), providing new understanding and new approaches for the study of dynamic imaging electron optics, thereby promoting scientific progress.

With this research, we established a relatively complete theoretical system for the school of imaging electron optics. It was different from the existing systems in that it adopted a unified point of view to examine and study the imaging and focusing, as well as the spatial and temporal aberrations of imaging electron optics. Our theory proved that, in both static and dynamic imaging electron optics, the spatial aberration is a composite of the paraxial lateral chromatic aberration (2nd order + 3rd order) and the geometric lateral aberration (3rd order), while the temporal aberration is a composite of the paraxial temporal chromatic aberration (1st order + 2nd order) and the geometric temporal aberration (2nd order).

In my report on the study of dynamic electron optics at the Institute of General Physics of the Russian Academy of Sciences, I said that there would be more than one road to Rome, and similarly more than one approach to study scientific problems. The "Direct Integration Method for the Temporal Aberration" theory proposed by the Chinese side started to the east, and the " τ Variation Temporal Aberration" theory proposed by the Russian side set out to the west. After a long journey, they finally met in Rome, and got the same result. That was called different routes to the same destination. The colleagues from the photoelectronics department of the Institute of General Physics of the

Russian Academy of Sciences were very happy. They said that after listening to my report, they became assured of their " τ Variation Temporal Aberration" theory.

With this research, we have established a relatively complete theoretical system of imaging electron optics not only in static electron optics with wide beam focusing, but also in dynamic electron optics with wide beam focusing. Different from the existing theoretical system, we used a unified viewpoint to investigate and study the imaging and focusing, spatial aberration and temporal aberration of the imaging electron optical system. Our theory rigorously proved that for both static imaging electron optics and dynamic imaging electron optics, the spatial aberration is a combination of paraxial lateral chromatic aberration and geometric lateral aberration, while the temporal aberration is the combination of paraxial temporal chromatic aberration and geometric temporal aberration; that in both the lateral and temporal aberrations, the spatial resolution or the temporal resolution is directly related to the field strength at the cathode surface. Our study confirmed that the second-order paraxial lateral chromatic aberration caused by the initial energy dispersion of photoelectron emission is the fundamental limit of the spatial resolution of the image tube; meanwhile, the first-order paraxial temporal aberration caused by the initial energy dispersion of photoelectron emission chromatic aberration, known as time-flight dispersion, restricts the temporal resolution of high-speed photographic image converter tube cameras.

The importance of thought can be seen from our research on this issue. First of all, we linked the static problem of wide beam electron optics to the dynamic problem, and then realized that they are two characteristics of the same thing (i. e. , the initial energy dispersion of photoelectrons escaping from the cathode surface) on a certain imaging surface, namely the spatial aberration and the temporal aberration. Then, we unified the two aberrations in definition and reached a scientific conclusion after a series of comparisons.

I keenly felt that, as a scientific worker, he should try to make his scientific research correctly descriptive of the objective properties of nature and the nature of the laws of motion, pursue a higher degree of generalization, and try their best to uphold the aesthetic principle in science, namely harmony, simplicity, and symmetry as the ultimate goals of their study.

So much for our achievements and contributions in the study of dynamic electron optics. Interested readers may refer to the literature [15] – [17].

Here, by the way, I would like to talk about some of my feelings about scientific cooperation with Russian scientists. In the autumn of 1995, Prof. Schelev from the Institute of General Physics of the Russian Academy of Sciences introduced Dr. Monastyrski M. A from his laboratory to visit our institute. He was a famous Russian electron optics expert, both in theory and computer-aided design he got high achievements. I asked him to lecture specifically for my graduate students, and I acted as a interpreter. At that time, I introduced to him my newly published monograph "*Electron Optics with Wide Electron Beam Focusing*" and "*Focusing and Imaging with Wide Electron Beams—Selected Papers on Electron Optics by Zhou Liwei*," which he appreciated very much. I frankly stated that I abandoned the concept of traditional third-order geometric lateral aberration in the study of imaging electron optics, and replaced it with the second-order plus the third-order paraxial lateral aberration, supplemented by third-order geometric lateral aberration concept.

I was very happy that after I presented the paper "Electron Optics of Electromagnetic Focusing Concentric Spherical Systems" at the London International Conference on Photoelectronic Imaging Devices in September 1978, the Russian electron optics community also became interested in the electron optics of concentric spherical systems. I remembered one day, when I was having dinner with Dr. Monastyrski, he suddenly said to me, "Both Britain, the United States, Germany and Japan have not achieved much in the study of imaging electron optics, and I can not see any important treaties and contributions. I think that in this world, those who really understand imaging electron optics have not achieved much, only you and me. No other country is worth it. In this field, there are only two people who are second to none, me in Russia and you in China. Both of us have our own contributions. " He added: "I read the books and articles you wrote, and your research has formed a school of science. " At the time, his words took me by surprise. But my mind was very clear, and I would not be ignorant because of the praise of outsiders. He sincerely hoped that I could have a scientific collaboration with them in imaging electron optics.

Later, he and Prof. Schelev warmly recommended me to their teacher, the Nobel Prize winner academician Prokhorov, including the congratulatory letter that was drafted to me later. At the beginning of the 21st century, at the invitation of Prof. Schelev and Dr. Monastyrski from the Institute of General Physics of the Russian Academy of Sciences, I conducted scientific collaboration with them on dynamic imaging electron optics, and obtained a lot of achievements and progress. This cooperation has also enabled me to unify the theories of static imaging electron optics and dynamic imaging electron optics, forming a relatively complete theoretical system.

VI. On Scientific Research Methods

Now I would like to take this opportunity by the way to talk about my scientific research methods and experience. I believe that my approach to imaging electron optics has actually followed the scientific method commonly adopted by the master of physics. Specifically, it can be summarized as follows: Exploring and studying a simple and clear model, and analyzing the characteristics of the physical phenomenon corresponding to the selected model, to see if it can clearly describe the basic characteristics of the studied physical phenomenon, and reveal the main laws contained therein (studying the particularity, in which universality resides). Then, taking this model as a starting point for demonstration, to conduct detailed research including mathematical deduction on the theory outlined, and construct a new theoretical framework (model deduction). During the research, a set of complete theories is developed from a simple and clear model, evolving from simple situations to complex ones, and from special theory to general theory, making them more complete (from specificity moving to generality).

Naturally, the verification of the theory requires a practical test to examine its applicability. Since Newton, physicists have mostly used this research style from particularity to generality. Of course, that is not the only path followed in scientific research, but I believe that I have adopted the principle in my own research.

When I started to study imaging electron optics, I wasn't sure about the result, but my research goals or guiding ideology were relatively clear, that is, to solve problems in imaging electron optics from theory, calculation and design to practical application—design and calculation of image converter tubes and image intensifiers. In addition, I am tenacity and toughness, would persevere to achieve the goal.

Where should I start? Where is the breakthrough? Now it seems that my initial thinking was in depth and the direction clearer. I thought (just a vague idea back then) that if I could figure out every aspect of the electron optical properties of the bi-electrode concentric spherical model, I would be able to discuss imaging electron optics on a solid basis. Looking back on the past, I feel that I have managed to achieve a little bit of success mainly because of in-depth thinking in the initial stage. Fortunately, I was on the right track from the very beginning.

In theoretical research, we should start with the ideal model, solve the simple model first to thoroughly clarify the contradictions and laws of a simple model, before advancing to the more complex models to find common laws. On the basis of the ideal model of the bi-electrode electron optical concentric spherical system with electrostatic focusing, I moved on to other ideal models, thereby abstracting a set of theories in line with practical scientific problems. That is how I took my scientific journey.

From the particular to the general and then vice versa is actually based on the relationship between universality and particularity in philosophy. By studying the particularity of contradictions, clues with universal significance and regularity can be found, to furnish a solid foundation for studying their universality. However, research work must not stop at ideal models. When the work is extended to the study of axial symmetric imaging systems, both the image transference systems and the electrostatic and electromagnetic combined focusing cathode lenses become important issues in the research on imaging electron optics, and that cannot be avoided.

Below, I'll briefly talk about some of my methods and concepts on scientific research. In my own research experience and in tutoring graduate students, I have always approached a scientific problem by first clarifying its historical status, research progress, and remaining problems. Difficult problems can generally be divided into several aspects: first, those that have not been resolved; second, those that have not been resolved well or are reluctant; third, for the first two types of problems, we should analyze why they cannot be solved, or the reasons why they are not well solved and the crux of the problem, and then propose our own solutions. For problems that have been well solved, we shall study them in depth while thinking whether there is a better way or a better method.

The simple example of my inventing the flat coil winding cart that I mentioned above is to consider the way to solve the problem of winding on the flat resistance sheet on the electric meter, so as to propose to arrange the wires by imitating the procession of the guide rail of the machine tool. Its "entry point" or "breakthrough" is the method of screw procession, the scientific method and measure is called as "analog." It is a method of logical reasoning, which is based on the procession of the lathe screw to cut the object and use the method of screw procession to wind the wires on the resistance sheet to solve the problem.

Although the birth of the flat coil winding cart is a very common technological innovation, it contains various elements of innovation: the basic "knowledge" about screws that I learned at the National Shanghai Advanced Machinery Vocational School is the foundation, and the "association" and "analogy" are based on this, thinking out the idea of screw procession enameled wire and applying it to practice is "wisdom," designing and making the flat coil winding cart requires "ability," curiosity raises doubts and questions, perseverance and hard work are "spirit." Knowledge-wisdom-ability-spirit, these are the four basic elements that individuals must have when they innovate. The four elements are organically combined and then the innovation is born. Therefore, no matter what kind of level of innovation, as an individual, when realizing creation, it needs knowledge, wisdom, and ability, but also needs curiosity and enterprising spirit.

For problems that have been considered and well solved by predecessors, as if they were solved satisfactorily, I would ask students to look for its shortcomings, even nit-picking. I would ask them to think about it carefully, if they can open up another way or use another method, and try it, maybe better than them. When educating students, I think that we should give full play to the initiative and enterprising spirit for them, so that they can grow into a real scientist. I would also encourage students to transplant methods from other disciplines, maybe the results will be better and more advanced. All in all, I hope that students could have such a concept, that in scientific research, they must have the new creativity and their own idea (points, scheme and thought).

I think that in the solution of scientific problems, although not all roads necessarily lead to Rome, there should be more than one path, just like one climbs Mount Huashan, it's not the case that there is only one way. When people solve scientific problems through one way, don't think that this is a "swan song," and there is no other way. In scientific research, we should always be on the lookout for new ways, or even better ones, to address it.

I often find that in scientific research many young scholars always like to imitate or copy the ideas or methods of their predecessors (especially the prestigious ones), follow their ideas completely or with minor changes. They refuse to explore another way. Such kind of research is not impossible, but it can hardly be creative. I hope that when young scholars conduct scientific research, they should firstly think, secondly question, and thirdly try to find another way, instead of always following others around step by step. Of course, it is not easy to get rid of secular opinions, especially those told by the prestigious, written in books, and established by convention. It is easier said than done, but there should always be a spirit of doubt when it comes to scientific research.

As I mentioned above, scientists from the Institute of General Physics of the Russian Academy of Sciences asked me to help examine the authenticity and accuracy of their theory of " τ Variation Temporal Aberrations. " After accepting this task, I did not simply follow the scientific research routine to check the formulae one by one to determine their authenticity and precision. Instead, I proposed a new theory of "Direct Integration Method" for temporal aberration that was completely different from their idea. It meant examining the same issue from another angle, instead of staying in the rut of others. This is often a habit of "taking the old road to be safe," just like the Monkey King struggling in vain to get free from the Buddha's control. To jump out of the shackles and break the routine requires unrelenting tenacity and courage. Finally, my research showed that both the " τ Variation Method" proposed by the Russian side and the "direct integration method" proposed by the Chinese side could effectively solve the problem of temporal aberration. Although they were two completely different approaches, one being the variation approach and the other being the Newtonian approach, they both effectively solved the same problem from different perspectives, achieved the same goal, and came to the same answer. As you can see, there is more than one road to Rome.

As we all know, science is discovery and technology is invention. The so-called discovery, that is to say, the answer to a scientific problem originally existed, but it has been hidden and has not been discovered. The task of scientists is to dig it out. For example, for imaging electron optics, to study the motion of electrons under the action of electromagnetic fields, its traveling trajectories, imaging characteristics and aberrations, the basic starting point is Newtonian equation of motion and Lorentz force. If the starting point or initial conditions of the scientific problems under study are the same, the approaches can be different, but their final results should be the same and unique, perhaps with differences in their manifestations. Looking back 60 years ago, when I was studying at the Shedling Library in Leningrad, I investigated the research on the theory of the third order geometric lateral aberration of the cathode lens by electron optical scientists from various countries. Seemingly the results were different and all the scientists considered their own result justified. In fact, they had all studied the same problem, that is, the motion of particles (electron) in an axial symmetric electromagnetic field. Although the methods and approaches differed, for example, some adopted Newtonian (trajectory) method and others adopted variation (eikonal function) method; some expressed their results with a vector or a scalar; or they adopted different coordinate systems, and so on. On closer inspection, there was essentially no difference, so the results should be the same. In other words, the answer should be unique, and there should be no substantial difference. Back then, in order to figure out this scientific problem, I took many detours, made useless efforts, spent a lot of energy and time, and experienced unimaginable hardships and pains to prove the correctness of my theory, acquire a clearer understanding for these problems, and dare to comment on some of the fallacies in the literature. That is how I improved my understanding of this scientific problem step by step.

Our collaborative research with the Institute of General Physics of the Russian Academy of Sciences in studying temporal aberration of dynamic electron optics also illustrates the essence of scientific discoveries. That is to say, if it is a scientific problem, its solution is already exists, and the task of scientists is to discover it and dig it out. Of course, the means, ways and methods of discovery can be varied, but the answer should be the same, because it precedes the discovery. Above I described in detail the "τ Variation Method" (the Russian side) and "Direct Integration Method" (the Chinese side) to solve the temporal aberration problem of imaging electron optics. The methods and approaches were completely different, but the answer was exactly the same. Yes, that is a cogent proof.

Therefore, for a scientific problem, its answer should be unique, because the answer already exists. The task of scientists is to discover it and excavate it; so it is called scientific discovery. If someone claims to have the answer, then we have to check it for correctness first. If we find upon review that the result is indeed correct, perhaps we can consider whether there are other ways to obtain the same result, and examine which way is better. If there are multiple outcomes, we can examine which one is correct, or which approach or method is better. If the review proves that the result is incorrect, there are more room for exploration. Therefore, my point of view is to examine the past of the research problem in detail, find out the problems, and determine which have been solved and which have not been solved, so as to propose an entry point to this problem.

Of course, for a technical problem, the answer is not the only one. Because it was not available in the first place, the task of technology is to invent a new method, find a new way, and explore a new means to solve it. That is why we say technological innovation. But when someone else has proposed or created a method or approach, you have to come up with a new one. You shouldn't repeat it, or pretend that it is your invention. Otherwise, it will be plagiarism or "lift."

In addition, I think that in every aspect of scientific research, the logical thinking, especially the critical thinking is very important. Therefore, in scientific research, it is necessary to anticipate in advance what kind of results will be obtained if such steps are followed. If the result deviated from expectation or went against assumption, then there must be an error in a certain link, even in the assumption link. Second, we must always look critically at our own and others' problem in order to make progress.

Both scientific and technical personnel need to learn when solving scientific and technical problems, but there are some differences in methods and attitudes. In my opinion, for scientific issues, the focus should be on thinking, critiquing and questioning; for technical issues, the focus should be on learning, borrowing and creating. The former category is represented by Albert Einstein, who questioned Newton's view of space and time, and used the relativity of simultaneity as a breakthrough to propose the special theory of relativity. The latter category is represented by Steve Jobs, who advocated pirate-style innovation, that is, he learned all the advantages and strengths of others, and transformed them for his use. His iPad and iPhone are cogent examples. Those two types of people are also very different in character, way of thinking and attitude towards life.

The following section is a brief description of my scientific research ideas. I think that in scientific research, thinking about and asking questions should be the first and foremost. For example, about imaging electron optics, I have had a series of questions in my mind. For example, regarding the aberration theory of cathode lens, some literatures put forward the so-called the central aberration and the third-order geometric lateral aberration. It should be discussed what are the causes and which plays the main role? How to define the lateral aberration and the temporal aberration, and what is the connection between them; How to find the exact solution and analytical solution of the ideal model? There are many literatures on the study of the third-order geometric aberration of the cathode lens, why are they different, and which one is correct or more accurate? The aberration expression is complicated, can we check the accuracy of the aberration representation with analytical solutions? In addition, what are the similarities and differences among ray optics, narrow beam electron optics and imaging electron optics, and what are the differences in the processing methods? What are the limitations of paraxial optics? how to improve the calculation accuracy of the trajectory of electrons escaping from off-axis object point? What about the imaging, computing, and design of wide beam electron optical systems, etc. Those problems have been circling in my mind. It should be pointed out that, it takes a long period of accumulation to evolve from thinking to innovation.

Listed above there are some of my questions and thoughts on the research of imaging electron optics, some of which were raised in scientific research practice. Although the idea was not so clear at the beginning, as the research deepened, the thinking deepened, and the belief became firmer, and I knew the crux of the problem and the way and method of exploration. Therefore, successful scientific activity is good at thinking, asking and solving problems.

Here, I'll first talk about the attitude of scientific research. In my opinion, in order to study a scientific problem in depth, we must have a dedicated spirit and the ability to focus our attention on it. To achieve this, first of all, it is necessary to create a relatively pure research atmosphere, an academic atmosphere in which one can sit down and stare at one thing and leave other things behind. To this end, we must try our best to eliminate interference from housework, administrative chores and other external interference, endure loneliness and solitude, and to maintain a peaceful mind to avoid distraction, especially the temptation of bad habits and fame and fortune. Of course, in modern China, research beyond utilitarianism will be very difficult. But a person who devotes himself to scientific research will not dipped in fame and fortune. Secondly, when reading previous articles and studying the achievements of others, we must interpret the problem from a new perspective, and think about whether there will be new ways and approaches. We must let our thoughts break through the cage and jump out of the fixed pattern that has long bound people's thoughts, and the scientific problem will be examined from a multidimensional perspective. Thirdly, we must embrace a spirit of rational criticism, respect but not blindly trust our predecessors, free ourselves from the shackles of traditions and habits, and have the courage for criticizing others and for rigorous introspection. Finally, we need to have the spirit of "looking up at the stars" and courage to release our imagination. The reason is that "both new possibilities and examination of old problems from new perspectives require creative imagination. " Therefore, many scientific masters love culture and art, because of the recognition that "knowledge is finite, but imagination expanded by culture and art is infinite. "

In one word, we must be focused in thinking. Only without diversion can we dedicate ourselves to the issue being studied. The so-called concentration does not mean obsession to the extent of forgetting one's meals and sleep; it means bearing the scientific problem under study in mind all the time, and thinking about it consciously or unconsciously. When a person really keeps a scientific problem in mind, his thinking will naturally focus on the "problem." He would think about from all aspects and at all times. Perhaps as he gets onto a tourist bus while traveling, or at the first note of a symphony performance, a scientific idea and a new idea come to mind. More often, attending academic conferences and seminars and reading new literature leads to inspirations from new ideas, new perspectives, and new point of view, and consequently ideological resonance. At such moments, the idea of "try his ideas in my subject" often arises. I keenly feel that scientific research is a process of countless attempts and countless failures leading to eventual success.

I found that many young scholars only ask questions and think about them when they are at work, and never think about their own scientific problems after work. The so-called eight office working hours is unimaginable for a professional scientist. In addition, many young scholars think that they are very smart and brilliant, and that the scientific research is easy to grasp. However, they become easily discouraged after several failures, not knowing that new results and new phenomena may be discovered when they "enhance their efforts, thinking, perseverance and improvement." In my opinion, the truly innovative scientific research and real discoveries are really difficult. Therefore, we need to be fully prepared mentally. In addition, I believe that in order to produce high-level results, efforts must be made to create a highly freedom atmosphere for scientists to envisaging, selection of topics and experiments, and reduce or even eliminate interference and restrictions that are eager for quick success. Take the 2006 Nobel chemistry prize winner Roger Kornberg for example. He could devote 10 years to his field without any pressure for producing results. However, thinking is painful, especially when there seems to be no way out like being trapped in a labyrinth. Of course, thinking is also happy, because of the feeling of getting closer to the truth step by step.

Second, those who studies science know that questioning is the most important means of studying a problem. By thinking about the practice of predecessors and questioning them, one can put forward their own understanding of the problem and try to solve it. Therefore, for a scientific and technological personnel, the first thing is to learn to question, be good at questioning, and ask questions. In addition, they should embrace a readiness to learning. Because analogies, associations, and reasoning, as used in the scientific method, are all inspired by learning the theories, methods and means of others.

Also, we should have the courage to face failures and mistakes. I personally have experienced countless setbacks and failures, to acquire some correct understanding and knowledge. My experience is that the core of innovation is to have the spirit of daring to question and criticize for generating new concepts and ideas. Creative research is a mixture of numerous failures and rare successes, and the so-called progress of research is the staggering of one failure after another with an unfailing enthusiasm.

In my opinion, in scientific research, the important thing is whether you have your own thoughts (ideas, creativity) and your own independent thinking. Here, the most important thing is to imagine boldly and ask questions. Don't be afraid of weird ideas, and don't be afraid of the stirring of strange ideas. Instead, embracing a welcoming attitude towards new ideas. Only by asking questions and striving to solve them can we get original results. When thinking about a problem, the way and the method of thinking are very important. At this time, the dialectical materialism epistemology and philosophy of science will be of great help in raising and understanding scientific problems.

I'm keenly aware that being a scientist really requires some special character and indomitable courage. First of all, in exploring through the vast darkness, he can still emit an inner light, and he has the intelligence to illuminate the truth, that is, the capacity for quickly discerning the truth and perceiving whether a path is right or not. That capacity is called insight. Secondly, he has the courage to follow this inner light decisively, that is, the courage to decide whether to follow or not. That courage is called decisiveness. Of course, insight, decisiveness, and indomitable courage grow through trials and tribulations. Therefore, it is not easy to become a real scientist.

Finally, I would like to point out that every scientific research personnel has his own habits and inertia, and even tends to develop a certain fixed view of things and an attitude to deal with things. I sometimes feel that experience, habits and inertia can even hinder the acceptance of new things, by consciously or unconsciously rejecting and attacking it. We should be on guard against that scenario. Just as my favorite poet Su Shi had said, "If you don't know the true face of Mount Lu, that is because you are right in the mountain." Therefore, we should always be ready to learn the strengths of others, and refrain from laziness and self-conceit; more importantly, we should uphold a transcendent vision of reality. That requires a life attitude of constantly learning, constantly examining oneself, and bravely embracing new things.

Here, I would like to talk about the association of innovation with "intuition" and "inspiration." Albert Einstein once said: "I believe in intuition and inspiration." Based on his own scientific creation practice, he has repeatedly emphasized that in the process of scientific invention and creation, there is no "logical" bridge between scientific observation and experimentation to the escape of a novel insight, and one must resort to intuition and inspiration. In this regard, I have said many times that we Chinese scientific and technological colleagues are not inferior to their foreign counterparts in "intuition" and "inspiration," especially the intelligence of my compatriots, are not inferior to their foreign counterparts. However, they seem to be somewhat lacking in "learning" and "accumulation," as can be told from my personal feeling and experience. In my contact with some foreign scientists, I found that they were knowledgeable about a lot of references and original materials, familiar with the history and achievements of the subject under study, and quick to come up with their own insights. I was truly impressed. In my opinion, they had a mental agility, a higher starting point, a clearer view of problems and a scientific hunch, which "enabled them to have an understanding and make judgment of issues without conscious reasoning. " That is the result of their outstanding capacity for "learning" and "accumulation. " I remember once when I discussed imaging electron optics with scientists from the Department of photoelectronics, Institute of General Physics, Russian Academy of Sciences, the issues under involved happened to be what I had been thinking about and thus familiar. I was able to handle the discussion with such ease that they joked that my brain could work as fast as an electron travels. However, I still believe that the so-called inspiration or intuition is the spark of thought triggered by long-term in-depth thinking about a certain scientific issue and conscious learning and accumulation. I don't believe in the saying that the pie falls from the sky.

Regarding the methods and approaches of scientific research, I have given a detailed description in the article " On the Approaches of Scientific Research", please refer to the literature [18].

Finally, I dedicate to you the inscription "Six Characters of Studying" written 20 years ago.

There are six key words in the way of learning: "Ambition, Diligence, Knowledge, Perseverance, Method, Creation."

Ambition produces aspiration. Ambition is lofty and unwilling to be inferior, devotion to science and education to rejuvenate the country as their own responsibility;

Diligence produces talent. Knowledge is good at diligence and neglectful in play, "Genius comes from diligence," and there can be no laziness for one day;

Knowledge produces seeking. Knowing and learning are endless, dare not be self-sufficient with one, humbly seek truth, and guard against impetuousness and pride;

Perseverance produces success. Perseverance, determination of the direction, strict self-discipline, not giving up halfway, then nothing is impossible;

Method produces abilities. Pay attention to the scientific method, be inclusive, interpret the subtleties, and know the works by seeing the subtleties, so as to be able to do great research;

Creation produces innovation. Only by being determined to innovate, daring to be the first in the world, thinking of what others can not think of, in order to catch up and surpass the world's advanced level.

Concluding Remarks

My scientific research started 60 years ago when I was studying in Leningrad, the Soviet Union, where I mainly studied the imaging electron optics of the bi-electrode electrostatic concentric spherical system with electrostatic focusing. My PhD dissertation was a summary of my research work in Russia. After returning to China, the "Cultural Revolution" began, and I could only study the electron optics of concentric spherical systems with electromagnetic focusing alone. And later I worked together with Fang Erlun, Feng Chitao etc, to study the electron optical system design for the image tube and image intensifier, and achieved some gratifying results. After the reform and opening up, Senior Engineer Fang Erlun and a group of graduate students such as Ni Guoqiang, Jin Weiqi, and Zhang Zhiquan and other new forces joined in my team, and our research pace accelerated. Since scientific research is new exploration, every step forward is very difficult. Nonetheless, we have made a lot of gratifying progress.

In the early 1990s, I organized my research results over the years and wrote a monograph "*Electron Optics with Wide Beam Focusing.*" After the book was published, it received a lot of praise, and high evaluation from 12 domestic and 10 foreign experts in the field of electron optics, as well as 3 national book awards. I also won national-level scientific and technological awards and honors for scientific and technological achievements. Some foreign experts sent letters asking me to translate my monograph into English or Russian for publication.

However, whenever I look back at my previous works, including academic papers and books, I always feel that there are many deficiencies—either the argument is not rigorous enough, or the research can be extended to greater depth. And I always feel unsatisfied. After the advent of the new century, I spent about 10 years in exploration, and extended static imaging electron optics to dynamic imaging electron optics, and formed a relatively complete theoretical system. I originally planned to write a relatively comprehensive book on imaging electron optics for future generations. However, after my election as a member of Chinese Academy of Engineering, I have been obliged to participate in too many social activities, and spent most of my time doing unproductive work. Although my fame steadily grew, my dedication to scholarship weakened. Moreover, what with the departure of my wife from the mortal world, what with various diseases, old age and frailty, I found the ambitions of youth gradually diminishing.

In 2016, on the basis of summarizing my lifetime teaching and scientific research experience, I published *Notes of Green Hiding Study*: *Emotion to Scientific Research*, which is a popular science book on scientific methods, including the methods and approaches to scientific research, how to learn, how to do scholarship, how to be a scientific person, how to apply for finds, how to write scientific and technological academic papers, etc. This book contains my personal experience, knowledge and experience. I hope to give this book to young scholars to inspire them growing up!

Today, as I recall the hardships of studying imaging electron optics, I am filled with emotion. When I graduated from college, I was given a technical assignment in designing image converter tubes and image intensifiers. However, the design requires a clearer understanding of the basic characteristics of the electron optical imaging system. This means that I had to become clear about its physical issues. Therefore, I had not only to study scientific theories, but also engage in system design and solve technical problems. I came from an engineering background and had a poor foundation in physics, so it was very difficult for me to study scientific problems. I have been trudging forward step by step on the long journey of scientific research. No one knows my hardships, except for myself. My wish is to establish a relatively complete logical structure and system in the theory of imaging electron optics, which will contribute to the progress and development of science.

The scientific contributions and academic achievements of mine (including my collaborators) can be roughly summarized as follows.

(1) In the field of imaging electron optics—electron optics of electrostatic and electromagnetic concentric spherical system, electron optics of combined electromagnetic focusing, electron optics of image transference system, aberration theory of cathode lenses, electron optical point spread function and modulation transfer function, general theory and aberration theory of wide electron beam focusing with large object surface having curvilinear axis, and static and dynamic electron optics of electrostatic and electromagnetic combined imaging systems, etc. has made a series of original researches and contributions.

(2) The original contributions in the spatial aberration theory of static imaging electron optics and in the temporal aberration theory of dynamic imaging electron optics have been made, unifying the definitions and theories of spatial aberration and temporal aberration, and proposing the following expressions for lateral aberrations and temporal aberrations:

The lateral aberration = the 2nd order paraxial lateral chromatic aberration + the 3rd order paraxial lateral chromatic aberration + the 3rd order geometric lateral aberration

The temporal aberration = the 1st order paraxial temporal chromatic aberration + the 2nd order paraxial temporal chromatic aberration + the 2nd order geometric temporal aberration

As a result, a relatively complete theoretical system of static and dynamic imaging electron optics has been formed, and the problem of imaging electron optics has been clearly explained from the logical structure. For those it is considered by domestic and foreign academic circles to have created its own scientific school.

(3) Applying the theory to practice, especially the electron optical imaging theory having curvilinear axis to the calculation of electron ray tracing, the developed software package of electron optical design and calculation for image tubes and image intensifiers, has paved the way for the independent research and development of low-light-level night vision devices in my country.

My scientific research has won recognition among domestic and foreign academic circles. In 1992, I was elected as a foreign member of the St. Petersburg Academy of Engineering. In 1993, after the publication of my monograph *Electron Optics with Wide Beam Focusing*, experts and professors in the field of electron optics and photoelectronics gave me high praise, including 12 from United States, Great Britain, France, Netherlands, Russia, Germany, and Japan, as well as 20 from China. They all consider it to be a scientific, innovative and systematic work, and many letters have been sent to me, requesting its translation into English or Russian for publication. The monograph won the 8th China Book Award in 1994, the first prize of the 7th National Excellent Science and Technology Book Award and the Nomination Award of the 2nd National Book Award in 1995. In 1994, I was promoted to full professor with special approval from the State Education Committee. That year, I published a special collection *Focusing and Imaging of Wide Electron*

Beams—Selected Papers on Electron Optics by Zhou Liwei, including 34 papers on 7 topics. In 1997, Samara Aerospace University from Russia awarded me the title of honorary doctorate. In 1999, I was elected as a member of the Chinese Academy of Engineering. In October 2000, I was elected as a foreign member of the Russian Federal Academy of Engineering Sciences. Academician Prokhorov, the Nobel Prize winner and President of the Russian Federal Academy of Engineering Sciences, said in his congratulatory letter, "You are the founder of your own school." In 2021, I was appointed a member of the Russian Academy of Engineering. In 2022, I published *Static and Dynamic Electron Optics—Collected Papers of Zhou Liwei on Imaging Electron Optics*, including 63 papers on 11 topics. In the collection, I wrote that "Giving a relatively complete logical structure and theoretical system to the static and dynamic imaging electron optics has been the orientation of my research and the goal of my life." That is also my resolution and pledge to engage in scientific research.

Today, when I look back on my scientific career and my research in the field of imaging electron optics, I think that firstly, I have been enterprising in vowing to seize the bridgehead of imaging electron optics and establish our own theoretical system, and that secondly I have studied a subject urgently needed by China, and with great scientific value and practical significance. To sum up, I have been able to make those achievements because I have always wanted to blaze my own path in imaging electron optics. This goal has always been an inspiration for me in my unremitting efforts, to combine personal ideals, aspirations and interests with the needs of the motherland.

As this article is about to be published, I deeply miss Prof. Juriye and Prof. Bykov of the Leningrad Electrical Technical Institute (LETI) of the Soviet Union, Dr. Семан О. И, who went to Peking University to teach electron optics as a Soviet expert in the 1950s, academician Meng Zhaoying of Tsinghua University, academician Wu Quande of Peking University, Prof. Li Zhenyi, director of Optical Engineering Dept. Beijing Institute of Technology, Prof. Schelev and academician Prokhorov, Nobel Prize Winner, from Institute of General Physics, Russian Academy of Sciences, as well as my collaborator, senior engineer Fang Erlun.

I would like to take this opportunity to express my special thanks to Prof. Monastyrski M. A and his colleagues from Department of phoptoelectronics of the Institute of General Physics at the Russian Academy of Sciences for their scientific cooperation with me. I am deeply grateful to Prof. Puzankov, director of St. Petersburg Electrical Technical University, Russia, Prof. V. Soifer, academician of the Russian Academy of Sciences and president of Samara Aerospace University, and his colleagues for their care and help. My sincerest gratitude also goes to the teachers of BIT, to my teachers in our college, such as Prof. Lian Tongshu, etc. Thanks also to my PhD and MD graduate students, especially Prof. Ni Guoqiang, Prof. Jin Weiqi and Prof. Zhang Zhiquan.

I sincerely thank the leaders of the Chinese Academy of Engineering, Ministry of Industry and Information Technology, China North Industries Group Corporation Limited, China South Industries Group Corporation Limited and Beijing Institute of Technology for their care and help.

As this booklet is about to be published, I would like to express my special thanks to director Zhao Qian of the Chinese Academy of Engineering. Ms. Zhao Dianhua and Ms. Li Weige of the Chinese Academy of Science and Technology Translators Association founded by Prof. Li Pei, as well as Ms. Hu Xiaojing of the School of Humanities of the University of Chinese Academy of Sciences for their contributions to the author's writing and translation process for their care, support and assistance. I am also deeply grateful to all the comrades from Beijing Institute of Technology Press: President Cong Lei, Vice president Li Bingquan, and editors including Chen Lihua, Xin Lili and Guo Shan. For their support and help, this booklet is successfully published.

When looking back on my scientific journey, I can not say that I did a good job, I can only say that I have tried my best. I think that if my mathematical foundation had been more solid, my mind more open, and more flexible, maybe I could have achieved more. At present, my thinking is still clear, so I still hope to complete the monograph *Static and Dynamic Imaging Electron Optics*. May the Heaven give me the opportunity, I sincerely hope that the path I have traveled can be of reference for young scholars, and I place my great hope in the young scholars of our country to create a brighter future.

References

[1] ZHOU LIWEI. Imaging electron optics of concentric spherical systems with electrostatic focusing, part A: electron trajectory equation [J]. Acta Optica Sinica, 2022, 42 (8): 0811001 – 1 – 8.

[2] ZHOU LIWEI. Imaging electron optics of concentric spherical systems with electrostatic focusing, part B: paraxial lateral chromatic aberration and geometrical spherical aberration [J]. Acta Optica Sinica, 2022, 42 (8): 0811002 – 1 – 7.

[3] ZHOU LIWEI. Imaging electron optics of concentric spherical systems with electrostatic focusing, part C: electron optics of multi – electrode concentric spherical systems [J]. Acta Optica Sinica, 2022, 42 (8): 0811003 – 1 – 8.

[4] ZHOU LIWEI. Imaging electron optics of concentric spherical systems with electrostatic focusing, part D: determination of the circle of least confusion and the ideal imaging plane [J]. Acta Optica Sinica, 2022, 42 (8): 0811004 – 1 – 8.

[5] ZHOU LIWEI. Electron optics with wide beam focusing [M]. Beijing: Beijing Institute of Technology Press, 1993.

[6] CHOU LIWEI (ZHOU LIWEI). Electron optics of concentric spherical electromagnetic focusing systems [J]. Advances in Electronics and Electron Physics, 1979, 52: 119 – 132.

[7] ZHOU LIWEI. Imaging electron optics of a combined electromagnetic

concentric spherical system, part A: Paraxial optics [J]. Acta Optica Sinica, 2019, 39 (4): 0411001 – 1 – 10.

[8] ZHOU LIWEI. Imaging electron optics of a combined electromagnetic concentric spherical system, part B: Paraxial aberrations [J]. Acta Optica Sinica, 2019, 39 (4): 0411002 – 1 – 8.

[9] ZHOU LIWEI. Imaging electron optics of a combined electromagnetic concentric spherical system, Part C: Approximate solutions of paraxial equation [J]. Acta Optica Sinica, 2019, 39 (4): 0411003 – 1 – 6.

[10] ZHOU LIWEI. Imaging electron optics of a combined electromagnetic concentric spherical system, part D: Asymptotic solutions of paraxial equation [J]. Acta Optica Sinica, 2019, 39 (4): 0411004 – 1 – 8.

[11] ZHOU LIWEI. A generalized theory of wide electron beam focusing [J]. Advances in Electronics and Electron Physics, 1985, 64B: 575 – 589.

[12] ZHOU LIWEI, JIN WEIQI, NI GUOQIANG. Research on the theory of curvilinear axial wide electron beam focusing [J]. Optoelectronics Technology, 1988 (4): 8 – 22.

[13] ZHOU LI WEI, FANG ERLUN, NI GUOQIANG, et al. Study of electron optical system design of image tubes in Beijing Institute of Technology. [J] The tenth Symposium on Photoelectronic Image Devices. The Institute of Physics Conference Series. 1991, 121: 383 – 395.

[14] ZHOU LIWEI, ZHANG ZHIQUAN, JIN WEIQI. Some problems of mathematical simulation in optimization design of electrostatic image tubes [J]. SPIE. 1995, 2552: 102 – 115.

[15] ZHOU LIWEI, LI YUAN, ZHANG ZHIQUAN, et al. Study of

temporal aberration theory of electron optical imaging system by direct integration method [J]. Acta Physica Sinica, 2005, 54 (8): 3591 –3596.

[16] ZHOU LIWEI, LI YUAN, ZHANG ZHIQUAN, et al. Verification of the temporal aberration theory of electron optical imaging systems with concentric spherical system with electrostatic focusing [J]. Acta Physica Sinica, 2005, 54 (8): 3597 – 3603.

[17] ZHOU LIWEI, MONASTYRSKI M A, SCHELEV M Ya, et al. On variational method for studying the temporal aberration theory of electron-optical imaging systems [J]. Acta Electronica Sinica, 2006, 34 (2): 193 –197.

[18] ZHOU LIWEI. On the way of scientific research [M]//Notes on hiding green building—My love in scientific research. Beijing: Beijing Institute of Technology Press, 2016: 9 –27.